THE NEWCASTLE UNITED QUIZ BOOK

THE NEWCASTLE UNITED

QUIZ BOOK

PAUL JOANNOU

MAINSTREAM PUBLISHING

First published in Great Britain in 1988 by
MAINSTREAM PUBLISHING COMPANY (EDINBURGH) LTD
7 Albany Street, Edinburgh EH1 3UG

British Cataloguing in Publication Data
Joannou, Paul
The Newcastle United quiz book.
1. England. Association football.
Clubs: Newcastle United Football Club.
I. Title
796.334′63′0942876

ISBN 1-85158-142-1

Typeset in 11 on 13pt Imprint by Bookworm Typesetting, Edinburgh
Printed in Great Britain by Butler & Tanner, Frome.

NEWCASTLE UNITED FOOTBALL CO LTD

Registered Office: ST. JAMES' PARK   NEWCASTLE UPON TYNE   NE1 4ST
TELEPHONE: (091) 232-8361   REGISTERED IN ENGLAND No. 31014   FAX (091) 232-9875

R. CUSHING, General Manager & Secretary

FOREWORD

by Willie McFaul

I was only too pleased when I was asked to provide a
few lines as a foreword to this first ever Newcastle
United Quiz Book, featuring some 1000 plus questions
and pictures on the Club.

The Newcastle United Quiz Book should be a marvellous
challenge for both United's young and old supporters.
Questions on the Club concentrate on the post-war era,
although the early days are not left out and the author
has ensured an interesting mix through United's compelling
history.

There is content to keep the most knowledgeable of fans
scratching their heads for hours.

Do you know,   Which United forward of the Eighties
                      has a cousin who played for Liverpool?

or,   Which ex Newcastle forward wrote a book
                      'Going for Goal'?

what about this teaser, Where can one find another Newcastle
                      United Football Club in Europe?

Previous books by Paul Joannou have been excellently
researched and well received by United fans, this Quiz book
will certainly be another.

WILLIE McFAUL

Manager - Newcastle United Football Club

Directors S. Seymour (Chairman) W. G. McKeag (Vice Chairman) J. Rush, A.F.C.
R. Mackenzie, Sir George Bowman, J.P., E. Dunn, G. R. Forbes, G. R. Dickson

ACKNOWLEDGEMENTS

The staff of *Newcastle United Football Club* are thanked for their co-operation and hints on ingenious questions. Journalist at the *Newcastle Evening Chronicle*, Paul Tully is acknowledged for his help in checking the text and inserting several brain testers.

INTRODUCTION

The questions in this first ever NEWCASTLE UNITED QUIZ BOOK are designed to provide hours of entertainment for fans of all ages with an emphasis on the post-war period as a means of ensuring a reasonable balance. Variety has been a key in devising the categories of questions, combining the straightforward with the unusual and intriguing. Whether sitting at home, travelling to football, sipping a pint in your local or competing in a challenge quiz, this book should be of great interest to all.

Whilst every care has been taken to ensure the accuracy of the information the compiler and publisher cannot accept any legal responsibility for any errors. If they have occurred, an apology is given in advance.

Questions in the book incorporate events up to the end of season 1987/88.

Questions

1   Who scored two goals against Coventry City at St James Park during March, his first double for the club?

2   It took United four games to record a home victory. They won 2-1 but against which club?

3   Which side did Mira score his first goal for Newcastle against?

4   Who did the Magpies meet in the Littlewoods Cup?

5   Which youngster made his debut as substitute in the 2-0 victory over Spurs in January 1988?

6   Which personality returned to Gallowgate for the first time since 1984?

7   Two of Newcastle's junior players appeared for England during the season. Can you name them?

8   Ian Bogie scored his first goal in November for the Magpies, against whom?

9   Against which club did United clinch their trip to Wembley in the Centenary Classic after a dramatic 90 minutes at St James Park?

10 United played this Scottish club in a challenge match during March. They won 1-0. Which stadium was the game played at?

RECENT EVENTS . . . I

11 September 1st 1984 was a memorable day for Newcastle fans. Why?

12 Name three United stars in the last three years to start their career with Wallsend Boys' Club.

13 11 Players made their debut for United in season 1986/87. Name three defenders.

14 Who appeared 57 times for Manchester United and another 51 times as substitute?

15 Who was nicknamed "Rambo"?

16 Which club did United face in their debut in the Full Member's Cup?

17 Which former United player made his debut for England in 1988?

18 In 1986/87 United started the season with a new record. What?

19 Which player was signed from a London club in 1987, the fee being decided by Tribunal?

20 Who was the last Newcastle player to have a testimonial match at St James Park?

CURRENT STARS

21 A player from the 1987/88 season cost United £5,000 from Carlisle in 1982. Who is he?

22 Which United star started his career with Arsenal and Orient?

23 This player appeared for Spurs, Southend, Bristol Rovers and Cardiff before joining United.

24 His middle name is Victor. Who is he?

25 Name three Cockneys in United's first team squad in 1987/88.

26 In what season did Willie McFaul last play for the club?

27 Who is nicknamed "Bud"?

28 28 November 1988 marks this Newcastle-born player's birthday. Who is he?

29 Whose birthday is on 2 January 1968, another Geordie by birth?

30 Which United player was born in Scotland's capital city?

CLUB FACTS . . . I

31 In which four seasons have Newcastle won the Football League Championship?

32 When did Newcastle United first play under that title? Was it in 1882, 1888 or 1892?

33 United have appeared in a record 11 FA Cup finals. What was the last final in which United did not concede a goal and in which year?

34   United turned pro' in 1889 and became a Limited Company in 1890, but when were they actually formed and under what title?

35   The club's youth side have twice won the FA Youth Cup. In which years?

36   United have won promotion from Division Two on four occasions. In which season did they lift the Second Division Championship?

37   The Magpies have appeared in 13 FA Cup semi-finals and lost on only two occasions. Once was in 1909; when was the other and who were the opposition?

38   The club has won the FA Charity Shield only once. Was it in 1933, 1909, 1910 or 1953?

39   The black'n'whites brought home the Football League War Cup in 1941. True or False?

40   The Magpies have won the Central League Championship once. In which year?

CLUB FIRSTS

41   When did United first win the FA Cup?

42   United's first victory in League football was a 6-0 win over Arsenal in 1893. True or False?

43   Who did the Magpies oppose on their debut in European competition in 1968 and what was the scoreline?

44   It took a foreign team 17 years to record United's first defeat on tour. Which club inflicted a 3-2 defeat in 1921?

45   Who scored United's first hat-trick in the Football League Cup? Was it Ivor Allchurch, Malcolm Macdonald, Alan Gowling or Ron McGarry?

46   Who was the Magpies' first substitute to make an appearance? The game was against Northampton in September 1965.

47   A Welshman saved a penalty on his first appearance for United in March 1961. What was his name?

48   Who became United's first six-figure transfer in 1969 by joining the club for £100,000?

49 When was the first time United played at Wembley?
50 Where did United go when they sailed on their first tour abroad in 1904?

WHO'S WHO . . . 1

51 A one-club man who played 412 games for United between 1963 and 1978. He won a Fairs Cup medal but missed both 1974 and 1976 Cup finals through injury. Who is he?

52 This player joined Newcastle as a teenager in 1970 and went on to clock over 250 games for the Magpies from midfield and up front.

53 One of several great full-backs to have served United. Was with Newcastle for over 40 years as a player and coach. First joined United in 1938. Who?

54 This forward netted 400 goals at all levels of senior soccer before the war. United's top scorer for five years in succession and a past skipper.

55 A Yorkshireman, he cost United £250,000 in 1986. Started with Burnley but spent most of his career with his home town club.

56 With Newcastle for two spells and turned out in 259 games. Five feet seven inches, he was eight years with his previous club in Yorkshire before heading for Tyneside.

57 A home-grown product, this player burst on to the scene in 1974 as a teenager. Appeared for the England "B" side with United before a £330,000 move.

58 United's most capped player. With United from 1949 to 1963, this copper-haired defender was described once as "a gentleman of the game".

59 Won over 50 caps for his country, he cost Newcastle £100,000 in 1978. Appeared for Preston North End, Rotherham, Peterborough and Cardiff amongst others.

60 Spent over 40 years in football; as a player virtually a one-club man with United but as a manager moved from club to club. Scored on his debut as centre-forward but served Newcastle best from defence.

13

61 Where was Paul born?

62 In what year was he born?

63 Which Boys' Club did he join Newcastle United from?

64 Against which club did he make his United first-team debut as sub in 1985?

65 Against which club did Gascoigne score his first goal?

66 True or False? He appeared for England at youth level.

67 When Gascoigne was capped by England Under-21s he scored on his debut. Against which country was it?

68 Against which club did Paul skipper United to FA Youth Cup victory in 1985?

69 Gascoigne scored two goals in each successive match during the past season, both in January. Against which two clubs did he score the goals?

70 Paul was sent off twice during the 1987/88 season. Against which clubs did it happen?

71   Ray Clarke and Mick Martin scored the goals in a 2-1 FA Cup 4th Round victory over this club in 1981.

72   Two of United's full-backs were among the scorers in a 4-3 extra-time victory over Colchester in 1982. Name them.

73   Two clubs have knocked United out of the FA Cup during the Eighties by 4-0. Name the teams.

74   A United player scored against his former club in this FA Cup 3rd Round tie in January 1985. Who was the player and against which club did he score?

75   Newcastle defeated this Second Division club 5-0, their best victory in the FA Cup for many years. Which side received the drubbing and in which season?

76   United have played one club twice in different seasons in the Eighties and lost both ties. Which club was it?

77   In 1986/87 United faced this side. In charge was a former star at St James Park. Who was he and which club did he manage?

78   United faced these players in an eighties Cup-tie; Kelly, Brazil, Allardyce. Which side did Newcastle face?

79   United have fielded three FA Cup goalkeepers during the era. Name them.

80   Who netted both goals in a 2-1 victory over Sheffield Wednesday in season 1980/81?

UNITED MASTERMIND . . . I

81   Who holds the record for the most appearances in the League Cup or subsequent Cup competitions?

82   Name two of the three players who appeared in all five Cup finals prior to the First World War.

83   Three United men have played for and then managed a Cup-winning side. Name them.

84   Since 1960 only five past England schoolboy internationals from Newcastle or Northumberland have turned out for United's first team. Name three.

85 The two biggest attendances at an abandoned game in English football, 63,000 and 54,500, both feature Newcastle. Can you name the fixtures?

86 In the Test Match series of 1898 to decide promotion to Division One, United battled it out with three other clubs. Name the three sides.

87 Which United player and former England international scored a hat-trick on the last day of his football League career, in an 8-1 victory over Swansea in 1939?

88 In 1926 United defeated which famous European club 6-1 at St James Park?

89 Which club missed a record three penalties against United in 1912?

90 What was so special about Newcastle's 3-0 win over Bristol City in April 1910?

UNITED MIX

91 A Newcastle player became the first captain to be suspended from an FA Cup final, and miss the game. Who is he?

92 Which United player was manager at Gateshead when they were voted out of the Football League in 1960?

93 Who appeared in the 1955 Cup final with a broken wrist?

94 Which Magpie face of the Sixties had played on all 92 Football League grounds by the age of 25?

95 Which side have Newcastle met the most in Division One football?

96 On 15 November 1958, United flew for the first time to an away game. Where did they play?

97 Four pre-war Newcastle centre-forwards have also played for Grimsby Town. Can you name two?

98 Who scored United's 5,000th League goal in September 1981 at Norwich?

99 Which Newcastle United manager had a superstition in his playing days never to wear boots with white laces?

100 Two United junior goalkeepers of the 1960s later made it big at Forest and Everton without playing senior football for Newcastle. Name them.

101 Only three United players have scored goals in World Cup finals. Who are they?

102 This striker arrived at St James Park on an eight-week trial and quickly made an impression forming a good partnership with Varadi. He was, though, sent back to his previous club after five games. Who is he?

103 A South African left United for Peterborough United in 1979. Name him.

104 Which United striker is now the PFA's Education Officer?

105 He cost United £180,000 after spells with FC Bruges and Sparta. Who is he?

106 This centre-forward was with United in the Fifties. He returned in the Sixties to help the side to promotion in 1965. Name him.

107 An England Under-23 cap in 1970 and past schools international. He scored 26 goals in 96 games for the Magpies. Who is he?

108 Who netted United's two goals in the 1932 FA Cup final?

109 Which United centre-forward reached the League War Cup final with Sunderland in 1942?

110 This player is one of only three to have netted with their first touch in international football.

PICTURE QUIZ . . . I

111 A United utility player.

112 A full-back from Tees-side.

113 Player and coach with
Newcastle United.

114 A past Scottish international.

115 Once a winger,
now an established full-back.

116 Non-league signing by Bill McGarry.

117 Who is this midfielder tackling Tottenham's Keith Osgood
in 1976?

118 Who is this United defender keeping Trevor Francis at bay?

119 United v. Stoke City. Name United's players opposing
Geoff Hurst and Terry Conroy.

120 A forward who came from the ranks.

121 Name four of the five England internationals capped with Newcastle United since World War Two.

122 Who is United's most capped player for any country with 40 games to his name?

123 Name two Newcastle skippers who have also captained Scotland; one recent, one old-timer.

124 United had seven players capped during season 1971/72. Who are they? Three were Irish, one Welsh, two Scots and one English.

125 Can you name four post-war foreign internationals to appear for United's League or Cup line-up?

126 Three Magpie centre-forwards have scored hat-tricks for an England or Football League side since the war. Who are they?

127 In 1987/88 United possessed six full international players. Name them.

128 Alan Kennedy appeared for an England line-up when a Newcastle United player. True or False?

129 Who was United's first England Under-23 cap in 1958?

130 Joe Allon, Neil McDonald, Wes Saunders and Paul Stephenson have one thing in common. What is it?

What happened on the following dates?

131 22 April 1957 – Farewell . . . 1

132 2 November 1977 – Double Dutch

133 9 November 1938 – England victory

134 14 August 1971 – Double debut

135 17 May 1984 – Farewell . . . 2

136 11 September 1968 – 4-0 start

137 12 December 1925 – Star centre-forwards

138 21 August 1971 – Instant hero

139 10 May 1967 – Stars galore

23

UNITED IN THE EIGHTIES . . . I

141 United's first game in the Eighties was a 3-1 New Year's Day victory at St James Park. Who were the opposition?

142 United's top scorer in season 1979/80, he scored 21 goals including 9 penalties. Who?

143 This player made his debut in season 1980/81 against Shrewsbury Town at St James Park in Newcastle's number 9 shirt. He went on to appear in 191 games.

144 Only five players have netted hat-tricks in the Eighties. Name them.

145 In United's promotion season of 1983/84 two players turned out in all 45 League and Cup matches. Name the two men involved.

146 Who is this? On loan to the Magpies for their return to Division One in 1984/85, he scored once and later played on the south coast with Pompey.

147 Name United's World Cup stars in Mexico during 1986.

148 Newcastle's heaviest defeat of this period occurred at West Ham in April 1986. Name the Magpies' three goalkeepers used in the 1-8 hammering.

149 This player was signed for a record fee. He was born near Rotherham and was a former bricklayer. Who is he?

150 Darren Jackson scored his first goal for United in a 4-0 win in season 1986/87. Against which club?

SCOTS CONNECTION . . . I

151 Name three post-war Scottish international defenders who have turned out for United.

152 Name three post-war Scottish international forwards who have worn the black'n'white shirt.

153 Name three post-war Scottish international midfield men to have played for United.

154 Who is United's most capped Scot with 16 appearances?

155 Willie Cowan, Bobby Mitchell and Ronald Orr, three Scots internationals, have one thing in common. What?

156 There were three Scots in United's first-team pool last season. Name them.

157 Which Newcastle player once scored five goals for Scotland against Northern Ireland?

158 Name two of the three Scots to manage United.

159 Two former United players now look after the interests of Cowdenbeath. Who are they?

160 What was the only Scottish club United played in seven games in the Anglo-Scottish Cup of 1975/76 and 1976/77?

MIX-UP . . . I

Rearrange the letters to find a United player

161 U L P A   D R G O A D D : Life saving striker

162 N R A K F   N A R B N N E : Tourist attraction

163 R Y T E R   T H B T I B I : A bit of the Hibs perhaps

164 H O N J   S A G R C G : Northumberland has plenty of these

165 L U P A   N E T O P E S H N S : Bridged the Tyne among other feats

166 V E N I K   E N G E A K : Breakfast special

167 N A Z R F   N E K E N O : Man from the bulbfields

168 I N O R N E   P I N O S S M : Pools expert

169 R A N E R D   C O S A N K J : Athletics is well known to him

170 L O N I C   C H E V I T : Edwardian great

EARLY HISTORY

171 Two pioneer clubs amalgamated to form Newcastle East End. Who were they?

172 Where was the meeting held that resulted in a new name being chosen for Newcastle East End?

173 In the summer of 1893 Newcastle United were elected to Division Two. Can you name one other of the clubs elected to the Football League with United?

174 The first coloured team to visit Britain played United in 1899. What was the name of this South African combination?

175 United were fined a record £750 by the Football League in 1924. Why?

176 Which League did United's reserves compete in before joining the Central League?

177 When did United join the Central League?

178 Who scored United's first two goals in League football in the 2-2 draw with Arsenal?

179 Newcastle West End signed two Scottish internationals in the days before Newcastle United. Name one of the pair.

180 United faced only eight players and no recognised goalkeeper for part of a Division Two game in February 1896. Who were the opposition?

FOOTBALL LEAGUE CHAMPIONS

181 When did United last win the League Championship?

182 For that season United changed captains. Who were the two players involved?

183 This man netted five hat-tricks that year. Who was he?

184 When was the last time United finished in the top four of Division One? Was it in 1938, 1951, 1968 or 1976?

185 Newcastle have topped the table only three times since the war during the season. In which season did they last do it?

186 In 1908/09 United won the title but what was so unusual about the victory?

187 The Magpies first lifted the trophy in 1905. They in fact almost won "The Double". Who defeated United in the FA Cup final?

188 In 1906/07 United won the Championship, but again caused

sensation during the season. What happened?

189 During those early years, one club challenged United for the title in their three title victories. Which club was it?

190 Which player who appeared in season 1987/88 holds a Championship medal?

MAGPIE ASSORTMENT . . . I

191 Which United centre-forward is featured on The Beatles record jacket, *Sergeant Pepper*?

192 Who holds the distinction of appearing in three different Cup finals for three different clubs in 1951, 1953 and 1958?

193 Who is this modern star? His early days were with Pelaw and Clarke Chapman and his middle name is Roland.

194 Which United personality was Footballer of the Year in 1967 and Manager of the Year in 1974?

195 He made over 300 appearances for Workington before spending seven years with United. Who is he?

196 Which six managers did Willie McFaul serve under as a player and coach?

197 Which Director of Newcastle United was Football League President for seven years?

198 True or False? Sunderland once played a League game at St James Park against Middlesbrough and won 2-1.

199 When was the last time England played a full International at St James Park and who were the opposition? Was it in 1932, 1938, 1946 or 1958?

200 Who was captain and led United out at Wembley in 1976?

PETER BEARDSLEY

201 In which game did Peter Beardsley first appear for United and in what number shirt?

202 Peter was given four trials with League clubs before being fixed up with Carlisle United. Which sides turned him down?

203 Which NASL club did Peter play for?
204 How many games did Peter play for Manchester United?
205 Which Newcastle United player did he play alongside in Manchester United's reserve side?
206 Against which country did Peter make his England debut in 1986?
207 Which side did Beardsley score against when he registered his first goal for England?
208 What is Peter's middle name?
209 How much did Peter Beardsley cost United in 1983?
210 Who was United's manager when the Magpies let Peter slip to Brunton Park?

211 After his transfer to Tyneside in 1975 his previous manager resigned in protest. Who was the player involved?

212 A former captain of Middlesbrough, he cost United £140,000. Who?

213 This defender appeared in 259 consecutive games for his previous club before joining United. Who is he?

214 Which Newcastle centre-half of the Thirties later coached such clubs as Roma, Lazio and Torino and took Juventus to the Italian Championship?

215 Which United defender made his debut in a 0-6 defeat at Chelsea in 1980?

216 This defender won a European Cup Winners Cup medal in 1970. Who is he?

217 Which defender won an FA Amateur Cup Winners medal with Crook Town in 1962?

218 Who was called "The Rock of Gibraltar"?

219 Which former United favourite played for Whitley Bay in season 1987/88?

220 Who cost Dundee £100,000 in February 1988?

REMEMBER SEASON . . . 1982/83

221 United kicked off the season with a home fixture with QPR, Kevin Keegan's debut. Two players partnered Keegan up front. Who were they?

222 United had two five-goal away victories against which clubs?

223 Apart from Keegan, United fielded two other England international players during the season. Name them.

224 In the Milk Cup, United went out over two legs in the 2nd round and after extra-time. Who knocked the Magpies out?

225 At Christmas United signed a replacement on loan for the injured Keegan. He appeared on eight occasions. Who was he and from which club did he arrive?

226 During the season Arthur Cox introduced two 16-year-olds. Who were they?

227 What was so dramatic about a 2-2 draw at Oldham during October 1982?

228 United just missed promotion that year. Who did go up? Was it Leicester City, Fulham, Sheffield Wednesday, Wolves or QPR? Name the three clubs.

229 United's central defence consisted of two cost-nothing players, both signed locally. Who were they?

230 In the FA Cup a certain individual "knocked" United from the competition and allowed the eventual Cup finalists to progress. Who was he and why?

PICTURE QUIZ . . . 2

231 Who is this United player?

232 A Scottish international forward. Who?

233 One of Newcastle United's directors. Who is he?

234 A forward from the Seventies. Who?

31

235 One of United's Fifties stars, but who?

236 Whose is this face?

237 One of United's managers. What is his name?

238 A United defender clashing with Manchester United's Taylor. Name him.

239 A former United forward later to play for England in the Fifties. Who?

240 Who is this Newcastle player of the Sixties?

THE MEN IN CHARGE

241 Who was United's first full-time manager? A Scot, he was also the oldest debutant in the Football League.

242 Which six United managers have taken the club to Wembley?

243 Name the three bosses who have been in charge when the Magpies were relegated.

244 From Newcastle's 14 managers, which four also played for the club?

245 Which Newcastle boss fielded his son and nephew in United's first team?

246 Joe Harvey was in charge of Newcastle from 1962-75 and saw his team play in no division other than the First. True or False?

247 Who is this United manager? Tall, thin, angular-faced, he hails from the Staffs town of Hednesford. He won League Cup medals and started coaching at Gay Meadow.

248 Who succeeded Richard Dinnis at St James Park in 1978?

249 Which United bosses hold full international caps?

250 Which club did Arthur Cox appear for as a player, and which side did United secure him from as manager in 1980?

UNITED IN THE LEAGUE CUP

251 United's first fixture in the Football League Cup was on 10 October 1960. Newcastle lost 4-1, against which Third Division club?

252 The club's longest game in the competition took 138 minutes during 1979/80. United lost after extra-time in a return leg with which club and how did they lose?

253 United's heaviest defeat occurred in October 1976. What was the score and who gave the Magpies the hammering?

254 During the Eighties, United were knocked out twice within three years by the same club. This team eventually won the Milk Cup in 1986. What was the name of the side?

255 United's opening game on their 1976 run to Wembley was

37

against Southport. One United striker netted four goals in the 6-0 victory. Who?

256 Still on the Wembley trail of 1976, what was so strange about United's goal in the 5th round 1-0 win over Notts County?

257 When Blackpool defeated the Magpies 3-0 at St James Park in 1972/73 one former United favourite and a future Magpie star played a big part in the Seasiders' victory. Who are the two players involved?

258 United lost twice in the space of four days during October 1971, 0-4 and 2-4, to a London club, once in the League Cup and once in a Division One match. Name the side.

259 Against Sunderland in the 2nd Round during 1979/80 this player netted United's equaliser in a 2-2 draw. Up to then he had still to make a full appearance for Newcastle. Who is he?

260 Who managed Bury when they toppled United from the League Cup in 1980/81?

UNITED MASTERMIND . . . 2

261 What was unusual about Newcastle's 4-2 victory at Huddersfield in October 1951?

262 United have appeared in five FA Charity Shield games but won only once, that 2-0 in 1909. Who were the opposition?

263 On the other four occasions United lost to the title holders. Name three of the clubs involved in the years 1932, 1951, 1952 and 1955.

264 In a friendly match against Brampton in 1898/99 United won 12-2. What was so special about the game?

265 Who has scored in every round of the FA Cup for Newcastle and in what year?

266 Three players have scored in every round of the FA Cup bar the final. Name two of them.

267 Newcastle's longest Cup-tie took 420 minutes to settle in 1924. Against which side were Newcastle playing?

268 In League or Cup football United had never met six clubs. Can you name three of them?

269 What have these famous names in common . . . Stan Mortenson, Bill Nicholson and Tom Finney?

270 In the successful Anglo-Italian Cup run of 1973, United met five different Italian sides. Can you name three of them?

WHERE DID THEY COME FROM?

271 Albert Craig cost United £100,000 in February 1987. From which Scottish club did he come?

272 Imre Varadi almost signed for Benfica before joining United in August 1981. Who did United sign him from?

273 United winger Albert Scanlon came from this club to Gallowgate in 1960.

274 Len Shackleton appeared for which team before joining United?

275 Scot Alex Reid signed for the Magpies in October 1971, from which club?

276 Mick Mahoney arrived from which side in March 1975?

277 Alf McMichael and George Hannah, two Fifties stars, were signed from which Irish side?

278 Mike Larnach was a big-money Bill McGarry signing in 1977. Which Scots club received £100,000?

279 Goalkeeper Steve Hardwick was a product of which team before joining United in 1976?

280 Terry Hibbitt joined Newcastle twice. Name both clubs he was with prior to signing for United.

UNITED IN THE FA CUP . . . THE SEVENTIES

281 United faced these players in an important Cup-tie of the Seventies – Lee, George, Davies and Nish. Name the opposing club.

282 United reached the 6th round twice in the Seventies. Who did they meet and in which seasons?

283 Who netted United's opening FA Cup goal of the era, in a 1-1 draw with Ipswich Town?

284 In the 1974 FA Cup final who won the invitation 3,000m race prior to the match with Liverpool?

285 United have been knocked out on three occasions by Third or Fourth Division clubs. Name two of these sides.
286 Where did the Magpies meet and eventually defeat Bolton Wanderers in the 5th round replay of 1976?
287 The Black'n'Whites met this club twice in the era, in 1974/75 and 1976/77.
288 What incident happened immediately after the tie with this club in 1977?
289 This winger only played one full game in the FA Cup for United, against Torquay United. He scored. What was he called?
290 In 1973/74 Newcastle played four fixtures on neutral grounds. Name the four stadiums.

AUTOGRAPHS . . . I

Can you name the United players with these autographs?

291

292

293

294

295

296

297

298

299

300

RECENT STARS

301 Which United player was hailed a hero in Worcestershire by saving the life of a drowning two-year-old?

302 Who was the Sunderland-born former England schools player who made his debut in December 1986 against Charlton?

303 Which former United star has recently been with such clubs as Husquvarna, Beerschot and Grantham?

304 Two former Magpie players appeared for Birmingham City in 1987/88. Who are they?

305 Which former United keeper was on loan at Roker Park in September 1987?

306 A United striker and a former England man had a spell with Finn Harps in 1986. Name him.

307 This six-foot defender made one appearance for the club against Everton in 1986/87 before being given a free transfer. Who is he?

308 Who, still at St James Park, started his career with Melbourne Thistle?

309 Which two Newcastle players joined Swansea in the summer of 1987?

310 Who cost Leeds United £45,000 in July 1986 from United?

MAGPIE ASSORTMENT . . . 2

311 Which club that United faced in European competition fielded names Papi, Larios and Felix?

312 Name four *Craigs* to have played football for United.

313 Which post-war United manager appeared in a friendly for the club in Ireland and actually scored?

314 Who wrote *Proud to be a Geordie*?

315 When did United last win at Old Trafford? Was it 1982/83, 1971/72, 1969/70 or 1958/59?

316 Which Republic of Ireland side have United faced in competitive football since 1960?

317 Four United players helped Sunderland win the division two title in 1975/76. Name them.

318 Three different players appeared in the Number 11 shirt in United's three major Cup finals since 1960. Can you name them?

319 Which former Newcastle player was in charge of Blyth Spartans in 1987/88?

320 Three former United men appeared for England against Israel in 1987/88. Name all three.

LOOSE ENDS... I

321 Who was United's top scorer in League and Cup football in successive seasons 1951/52 and 1952/53?

322 Name the two members of United's Youth Cup-winning side of 1962 who went on to play for their country at full level.

323 Who was United's caretaker-boss in 1977 following the departure of Richard Dinnis?

324 Who guested at centre-forward for Newcastle and opposed his brother at centre-half in the Tony Green testimonial match in 1974? Name both brothers.

325 Who was United's Player of the Year for two years running in 1973 and 1974?

326 Who was sent off within the first minute and a half, perhaps the fastest sending-off of all time, on 5 December 1973?

327 Name two Newcastle players to have amassed over 50 caps for Ireland during their career.

328 Who became Chairman of the Players' Union in 1980?

329 Who is the tallest player, at six feet four inches, to have turned out for the Magpies?

330 Against Inter Milan in the Inter Cities Fairs Cup of 1970, what colour strip did United wear at Gallowgate?

SAME NAMES... I

All the answers are United players:

331 A north-east community.

332 A European country.

333 Name three colours.
334 Three parts of the human anatomy.
335 The name of another sport.
336 Two American Presidents.
337 Two British Prime Ministers.
338 A wartime aeroplane.
339 Three historical personalities.
340 Two types of motor-car.

UNITED MIDFIELD MEN

341 Who is this player? Appeared 38 times from 1976-1978 before going to the States. Tall, leggy and a Gordon Lee man.

342 Name the United half-back who played only ten games for the club but who also played for his country against England at Wembley in 1970.

343 Now at Celtic Park, this United star won a Welsh Cup medal in 1981.

344 A real character. This midfielder once pulled down the shorts of a Bury defender while he lined up for a free-kick. 43 goals and 152 games before a record transfer. Who is he?

345 A Yorkshire midfielder of the Sixties with the same initials as "Special K".

346 This player went to Ayresome Park in 1985 after arriving in a cash exchange deal for John Ryan. Name him.

347 Who is this? A midfielder from pre-war times with 235 games for United, he later died in the Munich air disaster.

348 This player signed pro' in 1973 from the ranks but made it big far away in the USA.

349 He is the only midfield man to score a hat-trick since 1960.

350 Which schemer took United to the High Court?

44

351 Name this international forward from the Sixties.

352 Another capped player at St James Park. Who is he?

353 A United man in the colours of Bury.

354 One of Len White's replacements.

355 A Welshman from the 1950s.

356 A Scotsman from the 1970s.

357 Name the two United players featured in this game.

358 Who is this Newcastle defender?

359 Newcastle en route to Wembley. Name the 11 players pictured.

360 A Scottish international forward. But who?

361 In which season did United first enter European competition?

362 In that first season in the Inter Cities Fairs Cup the Magpies met two Portuguese clubs en route to the final. Name them.

363 In 14 home fixtures United have lost only one game, that in 1977. Who were the opposition and what was the score?

364 Who scored the goals when United defeated Glasgow Rangers 2-0 in the semi-final during 1969?

365 Six players appeared in every fixture during the Magpies' run to Budapest and victory in 1969. Can you name all six?

366 Former United skipper Jim Iley made one European appearance for United, against which club?

367 Two British clubs faced Newcastle and lost to the Magpies in the 1969/70 tournament. Who were they?

368 Which club did these famous stars appear for; Burgnich, Boninsegna and Facchetti?

369 United have faced two clubs from Hungary. Name them.

370 United have won on "away goals" twice. Against which clubs?

371 What is Kenny Wharton's nickname?

372 Who is this . . . "Gibbo"?

373 And what about . . . "Pop"?

374 Who was "Bobby Dazzler"?

375 Albert Bennett was called this nickname.

376 Who was known as . . . "Ollie"?

377 Who was this old star, known as "The Newcastle Flier"?

378 Another old-timer; who was "Peter the Great"?

379 Two famous strikers . . . "Supermac" and "The Mighty Wyn"?

380 Who was known as "The Laughing Cavalier"?

381 In which season was United's East Stand opened against Luton in an FA Cup match?

382 Who owns St James Park?

383 When did the club construct the old West Stand, demolished in 1987? Was it in 1900, 1905, 1908 or 1923?

384 In what year was the Leazes Stand demolished?

385 Which touring side defeated Northumberland 44-0 at St James Park in 1906?

386 United's inaugural game under floodlights was in 1953. Which club did the Magpies meet?

387 When did the club erect the seven-and-a-half-foot security fence around St James Park?

388 Which was the last continental side to visit Gallowgate, and in which season?

389 Who took part in the FA Amateur Cup final replay at St James Park in 1954 before a 56,000 crowd?

390 Which American team made an appearance at St James Park in 1958?

MIXED BAG . . . I

391 Against which club did United play their first League game on a Sunday in season 1983/84?

392 Which is the only team Newcastle have played over two legs in both FA Cup and League Cup?

393 The Magpies have faced several teams over 100 times in League and Cup football. Which club is not a centenarian in this list: Sheffield United, Arsenal, Chelsea and Middlesbrough?

394 True or False? United defeated Liverpool 9-2 on a Reds' Xmas visit to St James Park.

395 United defeated both Bradford City and Middlesbrough 11-0 in which season? Was it 1908/09, 1932/33, 1944/45 or 1962/63?

396 Floodlights have failed twice in United's fixtures, once in 1962, the other at St James Park in 1977. Name the two clubs involved.

397 Who did United defeat in the semi-final of the Anglo-Italian Cup in 1973? The result was 5-1, and who netted a hat-trick?

398 In April 1986 United recorded their heaviest post-war defeat. Against which club and what was the score?

399 United have never won at the following grounds; Abbey Stadium, Somerton Park and Gay Meadow. True or False?

400 £299,601 stands as United's record receipts for any game. What was the fixture?

MIXED BAG . . . 2

401 In the summer of 1982 United took two players on trial from Preston. Who were they?

402 Who appeared in over 500 games for the north-east's "Big Three"?

403 This international cost United £18,000 in 1969 from Scotland. He played in 64 games for Newcastle before heading for Ewood Park. Who is he?

404 This former star managed Apoel Nicosia in the European Cup during the Eighties. Who is he?

405 Name three Newcastle Welsh international forwards with the surname Davies.

406 Who holds United's record for consecutive appearances with 171 games?

407 Who did the Magpies sign in September 1982 after a spell in Hong Kong?

408 Name five Football League managers during the 1987/88 season to have played senior football for United.

409 Who skippered United's FA Youth Cup-winning team in 1985?

410 True or False: United once had a regular strip of red shirts?

Name the players and the club they were signed from?

411 A utility player and former United skipper. Played for United in 123 games before leaving for Merseyside in July 1978.

412 A centre-forward who arrived at Gallowgate in October 1979 for £175,000, having turned out for several clubs including Carlisle United, Coventry City and Plymouth. Scored only eight goals for United before signing for Pompey.

413 An Irish International, five feet seven inches, and born in Belfast. Cost United £75,000 and has worn the "Blue Star" on his shirt with distinction in over 200 games.

414 An old-timer who played for both north-east giants. Appeared for England as keeper in 1927 and signed for the Magpies in 1929. Won an FA Cup medal before rejoining his previous club.

415 He scored 58 goals in 187 games for Newcastle playing alongside a fellow striker who netted 121 goals in five seasons on Tyneside. United swopped D. Ford and J. Hope for his services from this club.

416 A household name during the Thirties. From an east coast club to Tyneside in 1928, he was capped for England three times when at Gallowgate.

417 Arrived for £110,000 in 1984 but did not stay long before heading for one of his previous clubs. He didn't kick a ball for the side United signed him from.

418 A centre-forward who netted 29 goals in only 36 games in the 1955/56 season. Cost £15,000 from this East Anglian club and left to join West Ham United in 1957.

419 A full-back who appeared for an England XI in 1980. With ex-United boss Gordon Lee at his previous two clubs, he cost United £80,000.

420 At St James Park in two spells; firstly on loan in 1982 and then in August 1983 after an exchange deal for Imre Varadi. Scored on his Magpie debut v. Norwich in 1982.

Name the players and the clubs they were transferred to:

421 He netted 153 goals for Newcastle in a career which spanned nine years up to 1962. Left United after a bad injury.

422 This player went to the States in 1982 after several brilliant and promising displays in a black'n'white shirt. Later was back in the north-east, including a spell at Roker Park.

423 He won a Wembley medal with this club after leaving Tyneside. Made 87 appearances for United and has been a promotion expert with several clubs recently.

424 United's top scorer in season 1980/81, he was a big-money buy but not a big-money success. Joined Londoners in 1982.

425 Headed 100 miles north in 1960 after 295 games for Newcastle. He went on to play another 300 times.

426 From the Hornets to the Magpies in 1985. This player left in the same year to the Throstles. 33 games and ten goals was his United record.

427 A spell on the continent followed for this centre-forward. Joined United from a Scottish club and left to join another Scottish outfit. Still playing yet north of the border.

428 A defender who rose from the ranks in the Seventies. Joined the Baseball Ground staff in 1978 and later headed further south in the west country.

429 Another defender, one who travelled afar after his spell at St James Park. Signed along with KK in 1982 and became a firm favourite with the fans.

430 A tall leader whose appearances and goals were limited after a £75,000 deal from Sheffield Wednesday. Joined a seaside club for £25,000 in 1987.

STAN SEYMOUR

431 In which season did Stan Seymour make his debut for United?

432 He made his name with Greenock Morton after United refused him a contract, but where was Seymour born?

433 What silverware did he help United win?

434 Did Stan ever win an England cap?

435 When did he become a United Director? Was it 1935, 1938, 1945 or 1948?

436 His son Stan Junior played for United's reserves in the early Fifties. True or False?

437 How many goals did Seymour score from the wing in 1926/27, a record for the Magpies?

438 Which Fifties Cup sides did Stan lead out at Wembley?

439 His other son, Colin, appeared for United's first team during the war. True or False?

440 What was Stan Seymour's nickname?

STAN. SEYMOUR.

UNITED IN THE FA CUP . . . THE SIXTIES

441 United's best performance in the Sixties was when they reached the 6th round in 1961. United received all home ties. Name three clubs they faced.

442 In 1962/63 it took the Magpies 12 attempts to play their 3rd round clash because of snow. Who were the opposition and what was the eventual scoreline?

443 United played this club in three different competitions during 1969/70 and lost 0-3 in the FA Cup 3rd round. Name the club.

444 Jock Wallace was keeper for this "giant-killer". Gordon Marshall was United's No. 1 and Stan Anderson scored United's goal in a 2-1 defeat. What was the year and which club were in opposition?

445 Almost 120,000 saw two 4th Round games with this club in January 1969. Owen and Young scored the opposition goals. Which side did they play for?

446 56,569 were at St James Park a year earlier to see the first meeting with this local club. The visitors won 1-0 and United missed a penalty. Who visited Gallowgate and who missed the penalty?

447 Only two players have scored hat-tricks for Newcastle in this period. Can you name both players?

448 United faced these players in a Cup meeting during the Sixties. Which club did they play for; Hennessey, Newton, Baker?

449 United played this club twice in the space of seven days; once in the League and once in the Cup. The Magpies won the League clash but lost the Cup-tie 2-1 at Gallowgate. The winners went on to Wembley. Who were they?

450 A former United striker of the Forties, and later an England man, was in charge of this visiting club to Gallowgate in 1969. Who was he and which club did he manage?

PICTURE QUIZ . . . 4

451 A Cup-tie in the Fifties. Who is netting and which club are the opposition?

452 United go ahead, but who is scoring the goal and against which club?

453 Who is sending a shot into the net in this meeting with local foes?

454 A Seventies Cup-tie. Where is the game held and who is scoring for United?

455 1966 against a London side. Who is the goalscorer, far right, and name the opposition. Which other two Newcastle players are in the picture?

456 Who scored with this header in 1961 and against which side?

457 Another goal for Newcastle. Who are United's players?

458 Who is this former Newcastle "All Time Great" pictured when a manager in the Twenties?

459 A Bill McGarry signing. Who is it?

460 How many of these players can you recognise? Secondly,
what are they celebrating and, thirdly, where are they?

461 Name the four Irish-born players on United's playing staff in 1987/88 to have made Football League debuts.

462 From which club did United sign Willie McFaul in 1966?

463 Which other famous post-war United stars appeared for this club? Name two players.

464 Who was capped by Northern Ireland in 1969 v Israel when in United's reserve side and only made four appearances for United?

465 Three United stars appeared for Ireland in the 1958 World Cup finals. Name all three.

466 This Irish midfield player appeared on 22 occasions for his country while at St James Park. Who is he?

467 Which Irishman can claim the longest period as a player with United, and how many years did he stay at St James Park?

468 Only one Irishman took part in United's 1955 Cup final. Who was he?

469 This former Ballymena man signed for United in 1948 and virtually won promotion for the Magpies that season with two goals against Sheffield Wednesday. Name him.

470 Three Irishmen, all full-backs, are in Newcastle's top six appearance chart with 432, 431 and 412 games respectively. Who are they?

FIRST NAMES . . . I

471 . . . . / DAVIES : From Norwich in 1979.

472 . . . . / EDGAR : One appearance at Derby in 1976.

473 . . . . / ALLEN : Six years with United.

474 . . . . / ANDERSON : England International.

475 . . . . / ROBSON : A striker, later with West Ham and Norwich.

SECOND NAMES . . . I

476 CHRIS / . . . . : Full-back of the Eighties.

477 JOHN / . . . . : Signed in 1977 from Scotland.
478 GEORGE / . . . . : A famous Gunner.
479 ANDY / . . . . : Cost United £100,000 in the Eighties.
480 MICHAEL / . . . . : Another who cost £100,000 recently.

SAME NAMES . . . 2

481 David . . . . : A blond full-back. His namesake also was at Roker.
482 Dennis & Mick . . . . : Both at one time to play for West Bromwich Albion.
483 Bill & Tom . . . . : Could well like the hot stuff!
484 Brian & Bobby . . . . : One a midfielder, the other a full-back. One from 1979/80, the other from 20 years before.
485 Joe & Brian . . . . : One a United man for over 40 years, the other a keeper at a time of depression.
486 Jimmy . . . . : Irish forward and also the namesake of a TV man.
487 Peter & Gary . . . . : Two youngsters to be given a chance in United's side of latter years.
488 Ian, Ken & Bobby . . . . : All post-war forwards.
489 Tom, Keith & Bryan . . . . : Three more forwards, all to play in London.
490 David . . . . : United namesake of a Division Two manager.

UNITED'S BACKROOM BOYS

491 Did United coach John Pickering ever play for Newcastle's first team?
492 Who was United's trainer for 25 years from 1903-1928?
493 Who coached the club and was Joe Harvey's right-hand man to promotion in 1965?
494 Who was coach when United reached Wembley in 1974?

495 Who is United's current commercial manager?
496 Only three past players have become club directors. Name two.
497 Who was trainer to United's three Cup-winning sides of the Fifties?
498 Which coach was at Gallowgate in two spells: 1966-68 and 1974-76?
499 Which club Chairman became President of the Football League?
500 Who refereed the Championship of the World game between West Bromwich Albion and Renton way back in 1888?

HALF-TIME

501 The record Football League victory is 13-0. United share this record with which other club?
502 Which famous club once changed into a Newcastle United strip for a Fifties FA Cup-tie?
503 In November 1974 an ex-United forward scored a second-half hat-trick of headers in his team's 4-1 victory over the Magpies. Who is he?
504 Which United boss went to Bogotá and created a sensation in 1950?
505 A future United player was a survivor of the Munich air disaster. Name him.
506 Who scored a hat-trick within 155 seconds in October 1946?
507 What was so significant about the Portsmouth v. Newcastle League game in February 1956?
508 And what was significant about the Portsmouth v. United clash in December 1931?
509 United's side defeated 0-3 at QPR bore a unique distinction. What was it?
510 Newcastle were the opponents in the last game at the Olive Grove ground, the former home of which famous club?

511   In 1905 United had four players in Scotland's line-up against England, a record for the club. Name three of the four players.

512   Which Newcastle player of the early Sixties caused the Football League to judge over a Norwich City accusation that United had sold him under false pretences, not saying he was a diabetic.

513   United fielded two ex-England internationals in the years up to World War Two. Both were ex-Arsenal men. Who are they?

514   On his debut against Bradford City at St James Park in 1908 this centre-forward broke his leg and never played for the club again. Who was he?

515   Which United legend led North Shields to the FA Amateur Cup at Wembley?

516   This former Newcastle and England inside-forward became the League's youngest player-boss at 23 when he was in charge of Carlisle. Who is he?

517   When United were knocked out of the FA Cup by Bedford Town in 1964, the non-League side's goalkeeper later became a famous manager on both sides of the border. Name him.

518   Within six minutes of his United debut v. Leicester in 1961 this player had scored an own-goal. He was at Wembley in 1987 with Coventry. Who is he?

519   This player won 12 England caps and a League Championship medal after he had left St James Park in 1948. He also represented Great Britain in 1955. Name him.

520   Which former Newcastle right-half was trainer with Brian Clough at Forest and Derby?

521   Who cost United £50,000 in October 1976 from Barnsley but only appeared once, then as substitute?

522 Name two United players to have appeared in the Olympic Games soccer tournament during their career.

523 Which United centre-forward also appeared in Test cricket v. Australia in 1921?

524 Which former goalkeeper was involved in the incident when playing for Bury that led to the retirement of Brian Clough?

525 Who had a spell with Swedish club Djorgarden in 1979?

526 Which former United utility player won a Finnish Championship medal in 1984 with Kuuysi Lahti?

527 A United winger at Gallowgate from 1958-1961 also played cricket for Leicestershire. Who is he?

528 Which Newcastle midfielder won the FA Vase with Blue Star at Wembley in 1978?

529 Which famed centre-forward scored four goals at St James Park for the Football League v. Irish League in 1927?

530 Who preceded Kevin Keegan as captain in 1982?

CLUB CONNECTIONS . . . I

531 ARSENAL: Which famous United player signed three times for the Gunners?

532 ASTON VILLA: Which United personality appeared in two League Cup finals for the Midland club?

533 CARLISLE UNITED: Which ex-United player scored the Cumbrians' first-ever goal in Division One in August 1974?

534 DARLINGTON: Which former Newcastle player went on to hold the Quakers' appearance record?

535 ARSENAL: What was so special about the game at Highbury won 2-0 by the Londoners on 8 October 1966?

536 LINCOLN CITY: Which ex-United centre-forward holds the goalscoring record for City with 144 goals?

537 ASTON VILLA: Two United players created transfer records at Villa Park in latter years. Who are the players that left St James Park for the Midlands?

538 YORK CITY: Which United forward holds City's scoring record?

539 BOLTON WANDERERS: What was so significant about the Wanderers v. United meeting on 18 April 1924?

540 FULHAM: What was the name of the brother of United's centre-forward of 1981-1983 who appeared for Fulham?

CLUB CONNECTIONS . . . 2

541 BRIGHTON: Which United centre-forward achieved Brighton's post-war scoring record with 30 goals in 1967/68?

542 HALIFAX TOWN: With 367 games between 1965-1974 this former United player holds Town's appearance record. Who is he?

543 LUTON TOWN: Who scored for United in the first minute of his debut at Luton in November 1957?

544 MANCHESTER CITY: In May 1926 City missed a penalty at Gallowgate. What was so significant about the miss?

545 MANSFIELD TOWN: In the summer of 1981 Mansfield signed three former Newcastle players. Name them.

546 STOKE CITY: Who became Stoke's first manager in 1923?

547 QPR: Name the four ex-Rangers players to be at St James Park in 1986/87.

548 PORT VALE: Which former United defender managed Port Vale to promotion in 1983?

549 PETERBOROUGH UNITED: A United winger holds the Posh record appearance of 482 games between 1968 and 1981. Who is he?

550 SWANSEA CITY: Three of four Newcastle players called Davies have all played for the Swans. Name them.

UNITED IN THE EIGHTIES . . . 2

551 In 1980 which ex-United player became the first man to win both the PFA and FWA Footballer of the Year awards in the same season?

552 Season 1980/81 was the worst on record for United goalscoring. No player ended in double figures and only two scored more than five goals. Can you name Newcastle's top scorers?

553 Name two players to have played for United in the last five years and who have also played in the United States.

554 What was the last senior England representative game held at St James Park? The year was 1983 and England won 1-0.

555 Who did United face in their debut in the Simod Cup?

556 Which club did United face for the very first time in 1986/87?

557 Who is nicknamed "Dickie"?

558 Who made his debut for his country in 1988 against Greece?

559 In 1984 United fielded a team for the Jackie McNamara testimonial at Easter Road. Who guested for the home side on that day?

560 Name the four players who wore the number 9 shirt in season 1985/86.

DATES ... 2

What happened on the following dates?

561 11 June 1969 – Foreign celebration.

562 5 February 1972 – TV nightmare.

563 1 January 1985 – Peter's day.

564 7 May 1955 – "The Plan" beaten.

565 5 October 1946 – Record debut.

566 1 February 1932 – Record Cup score.

567 3 September 1930 – What a return.

568 21 April 1986 – Keepers galore.

569 28 August 1982 – United reborn.

570 9 March 1974 – Cup shock.

UNITED IN THE FA CUP ... THE FIFTIES

571 How many games did United go unbeaten to create a new FA

Cup record during seasons 1950/51, 1951/52 and 1952/53? Was it 14, 16, 18 or 20 games?

572 Who did United play in the FA Cup semi-final replay at Roker Park in 1955?

573 In both the 1950/51 and 1951/52 Cup runs United reached Wembley after replays in the semi-finals. Where was the first game played in each case?

574 In season 1952/53 a Division Three side knocked United out at St James Park. Who were the giant-killers that knocked the Cup-holders out?

575 Who netted the crucial penalty in the semi-final of 1952 to send Newcastle to Wembley?

576 United faced this side three times in the 5th Round on their way to the final in 1955.

577 Who knocked Cup-holders United out of the tournament in the 6th Round of 1956 at Gallowgate?

578 The Magpies took part in two terrific Cup battles in seasons 1955/56 and 1956/57. Both games were away from Tyneside and both ended 5-4 to United. Who did United play?

579 Which one of United's Fifties Cup finals was shown live on TV?

580 United faced these players in a Cup-tie during the era. Which club did they appear for: McGarry, Quested and Staniforth?

REMEMBER SEASON . . . 1973/74

581 Which non-League side did United face at the second attempt in the FA Cup 3rd round, and where was the game played?

582 Newcastle United won only once at St James Park en route to Wembley. True or False?

583 In the Football League Cup, Newcastle had a 6-0 victory over Doncaster Rovers. One player netted his first goal for the club. Who was he?

584 This player made his debut for the side during February after a £150,000 transfer. He quickly departed, however. Name him.

585 Newcastle met Burnley in the FA Cup semi-final. They also met the Turf Moor club in the final of another competition. What was the scoreline and name of the tournament?

586 United's Cup run started to gain momentum after a 3-0 win at the Hawthorns. Who netted United's goals?

587 In the 6th round Newcastle met Forest. Who was sent off in the first meeting and who netted United's "winner" in the closing moments to make the score 4-3?

588 Where were the two replay games with Forest held and who eventually scored the lone goal that took the club to the semi-final?

589 At Wembley against Liverpool who was Newcastle's substitute and who did he replace?

590 Out of the 24 players on view in the United v. Liverpool clash, three men eventually swopped clubs. Name them.

PHOTOFIT . . . I

591 Who is this United international star from the 1930s?

592 A famous number 9 hero, seen in United's change strip of the Twenties. Who?

593 Newcastle won this trophy prior to the First World War. What is it?

594 Another international Magpie. Who is it?

595 No-one has played more for Newcastle than this player. Who is he?

596 Who is this black 'n' white winger?

597 This player spent 19 years at St James Park. Who is he?

598 Celebrations in the Gallowgate dressing-room. What was the occasion and name the 11 men on view?

599 Who is the United goalkeeper and the defender challenging
Vic Groves of Villa?

600 Action from St James Park in 1973. Name the opposition and
the United keeper and defender at the centre of play.

601 Which United player sailed around Britain in a 20-foot yacht and crossed the Atlantic in an equally small boat?

602 In season 1986/87 United were defeated by Sheffield Wednesday 3-2 at Gallowgate. Both United's goalscorers were dropped for the next game. Name them.

603 Which former United star is this? He possesses a record 68 Welsh caps and holds the MBE.

604 This United centre-forward's brother played for Blue Star in the 1981 FA Vase final at Wembley.

605 Name the player who has appeared for United in the Sixties, Seventies and Eighties.

606 This United centre-forward partnered two other Newcastle leaders at other clubs, Lincoln and Sheffield Wednesday. Name all three number 9's.

607 Which United captain holds a degree in Social Sciences?

608 Name eight Newcastle players who have taken part in a European Cup final.

609 What event housed the biggest crowd at St James Park in the Eighties?

610 Name a club in each of these countries to play in black'n' white stripes: Brazil, Iceland, Italy, Scotland and England.

611 Which club that United faced en route to winning the Fairs Cup in 1969 fielded these players: Morais, Chico, Dama and Marinho?

612 Who wrote *Football Inside Out*?

613 What was the connection between the two Cup final goalkeepers in 1932, United's McInroy and Arsenal's Moss?

614 Name two European League clubs to also be nicknamed The Magpies.

615 Which Chelsea player netted four goals against United in a six-goal second-half romp at St James Park in 1961?

616 Which recent United player's father appeared for Gateshead in their last League season in 1959/60?

617 The Magpies faced these players in a Cup-tie in 1976. Which club did they play for: McLintock, Webb, Parkes and Francis?

618 What was the name of Kevin Keegan's record that hit the charts in 1979?

619 Name three United football personalities to have been awarded the OBE/MBE.

620 United won the Tyne Tees Cup in 1944 against Darlington after the teams were level 3-3 after extra-time. How did United win the trophy?

TYNE v. WEAR

621 When was the last occasion Sunderland defeated Newcastle in a League fixture? Was it 1982/83, 1984/85, 1978/79 or 1979/80?

622 There was almost a Newcastle v. Sunderland FA Cup final in 1955. Can you name the four semi-finalists, and who defeated Sunderland?

623 Four former Sunderland players have been coach to United in the last ten years. Name three of them.

624 When Newcastle lost a penalty shoot-out to Sunderland in a League Cup-tie during 1979/80, who missed United's crucial penalty kick?

625 United's biggest winning margin over Sunderland at Roker Park is a 6-1 victory during the Fifties. In which season did it take place?

626 Who was the last Sunderland player to score a hat-trick against United and in which season?

627 Who scored two penalties against Sunderland in December 1967 to give Newcastle a 3-3 draw?

628 Only two United men have scored hat-tricks against The Reds since the War. Name them.

629 Newcastle have only purchased four players from Sunderland on a permanent basis since World War Two. Name them.

630 The last time Sunderland visited St James Park, United won
3-1. United fielded an on-loan striker. Who was he?

631 Which United and England captain was once asked to
become a Labour MP for a Newcastle seat?
632 When Frank Hudspeth appeared for England for the first
time in 1926 what record did he establish?
633 Where did United's pioneers Newcastle West End play most
of their football?
634 Where did Newcastle East End play most of their football?
635 Who served both West End and East End as secretary-
manager and played a big part in the rise of Newcastle's
pioneers?
636 Which club did United play in their first League match?
637 Who is the oldest player to appear for the Magpies and how
old was he, to the nearest year?
638 Which club did United face in their first Cup final in 1905?
639 United have fielded three players by the name of Harvey.
What were their Christian names?
640 R. Smellie was a United forward before the turn of the
century. True or False?

641 How much did United pay for Kevin Keegan in August
1982?
642 How many caps did Kevin win for England? Was it 55, 63, 72
or 75?
643 Which side did Keegan start with in 1968?
644 Which clubs did he appear for after Liverpool?
645 Where was KK born?
646 What sensation happened at Belgrade Airport in 1974?
647 In 1980 Keegan appeared in the European Cup final, but lost
to which club? Also, who did he play for?

648 What did he win in 1978 and 1979?

649 Kevin last appeared for England in the World Cup of 1982. Against which country?

650 His debut for United was against QPR, but who was the well known referee?

TRANSFER TRAIL

651 Which recent Oldham Athletic player joined United from Ipswich Town in 1974 and made 62 appearances from the centre-half position?

652 In the space of two years during the Forties United sold star forwards and smashed the national transfer fee. The amounts were £12,500 and £20,050. Who were the players involved?

653 United spent £200,000 for this international player in 1978, a new club record fee. A much-travelled individual who became a firm favourite with Tyneside fans. Who?

654 Who is the club's most expensive full-back purchase? He was signed in 1983 from a Second Division club.

655 This player only spent a matter of 86 days with the club, one of the shortest stays in United's history. Who?

656 Mirandinha played for several Brazilian clubs, two of which have opposed United. Name them.

657 When United signed Wyn Davies to create a club record fee of £80,000 in 1966, the previous record was smashed by £35,000. Who held that record?

658 Who joined the Magpies in February 1986 on loan and spent four months on United's books?

659 Which former United striker signed for Reading for £120,000 in 1988?

660 United signed this defender in 1973 for £20,000 after he scored an own-goal for his previous club against Newcastle. Who is he?

CLUB FACTS . . . 2

661 In which season did United record their highest number of victories? Was it in 1927/28, 1926/27, 1951/52 or 1959/60? How many was it?

662 United's biggest win in League football was 13-0. Against which club and what was the year?

663 Way back in season 1894/95 United registered both their heaviest League defeat, 0-9, and their worst FA Cup defeat, 1-7. Which were the two clubs involved?

664 United's biggest victory in the FA Cup, 9-0, was at Hillsborough in 1932 en route to Wembley, but against which club?

665 Which club have United recorded the most number of wins against: Arsenal, Sunderland or Manchester City?

666 The worst attendance for a League or Cup game involving United since the War only recorded 4,026 fans. It was a match in 1981/82. Who were the London opposition?

667 The Magpies' best result in any game was a 16-2 win over Alberta when on tour in 1949. True or False?

668 Which United player holds the record for the most goals scored in a career, netting 200 goals?

669 Have United ever gone through a season totally undefeated at St James Park?

670 Newcastle went a record 21 games without a victory, but in which season? Was it 1933/4, 1959/60, 1965/66 or 1977/78?

UNITED FAMILIES

671 Two brothers were at St James Park in the early Seventies, but although both appeared in the first team they never played together. Who are they?

672 Who are the only set of brothers that have appeared in United's side together since the First World War?

673 Whose elder brother, David, played rugby for Cardiff and just missed a cap for Wales which would have made a family double?

674 What was so unusual about the international brothers, John and Dave Hollins?

675 George Eastham's brother Harry played for United too. True or False?

676 Which recent United player's father was on the Magpies' books during the Fifties?

677 Who did Gary Kelly's father appear for?

678 Which United forward of the Eighties had a cousin who turned out for Liverpool?

679 Which famous Magpie centre-forward's son later managed both Chelsea and Sheffield United?

680 Which father and son duo jointly appeared 81 times for their country?

CUP ASSORTMENT

681 United have opposed one Second Division club in the FA Cup final. Which club was it?

682 Against Burnley in the FA Cup semi-final of 1974 United faced two players with past and future connections with Newcastle. Name them.

683 United defeated which European Cup winners both home and away in 1967/68?

684 Who was the Anderlecht wing-half who netted at St James Park in the dying minutes to knock United out of the Fairs Cup in 1970?

685 United have twice won the Texaco Cup. Who did they face in each final?

686 United have taken part in two FA Cup final replays, in 1910 and 1911. Where did the replays take place?

687 Which club did United defeat 7-2 to record in 1950 the club's highest post-war FA Cup victory?

688 United faced these players in a Cup-tie in 1978. Which club were they up against: Davies, Roberts, Shinton and McNeil?

689 Name Newcastle's goalkeepers in their five Wembley Cup finals since the War?

690 Which club knocked out the black'n'whites 1-0 in the War Cup semi-final of 1940?

PHOTOFIT . . . 2

Name the United players on these team-groups, from left to right, back row first:

691 United at the start of the 1971/72 season.

692 A 1968/69 line-up.

693 Bill McGarry's first-team squad in 1979/80.

694 The promotion squad of 1965.

695 United's 1956 line-up.

696 Who are these United players in 1962/63?

697 1952 and 11 of the best. But who are they?

698 England v. Scotland in 1933. Can you name the United player in the group? A former Newcastle player is also featured. Who?

699 Ten former stars pictured for a testimonial, together with one Roker Park favourite. Can you name all 11 players?

700 A Mastermind challenge – United's Cup-winning side in 1910. How many can you name?

701 Who was known as "Pedro"?
702 Who was "Cockles"?
703 A full-back nicknamed "Bomber"?
704 An England international called "Tadger"?
705 Which centre-forward was nicknamed "Kit"?
706 Who was known as "The Guv'nor"?
707 What is John Bailey's nickname?
708 Who is called "Dobbler"?
709 A forward called "Sarge". Who is he?
710 What was Jimmy Smith called?

711 Which England player with United appeared in two games for Somerset at cricket in 1939?
712 A United manager once coached Turkish club Galatasaray. Name him.

713 Who was in charge of United when they won the FA Cup in 1955?

714 Two England goalkeepers of the Fifties started their career at St James Park but never appeared in United's League side. Who are they?

715 In 1958 United's new floodlight system was opened with the Football League v. Scottish League challenge match. Which England centre-forward netted a hat-trick on the evening?

716 Who is thought to be the oldest player to appear against United, aged two months short of 50?

717 Name two players who have turned out for the black'n'whites since 1960 and have been capped by England at amateur level.

718 Who was Bill McGarry's assistant-manager?

719 United employed a caretaker-manager for nine months up to June 1962. Who was he?

720 Who is United's youngest medal-winner in a major competition?

INSTANT RECALL...SEASON 1987/88

721 Who were the two goalkeepers United signed on loan in 1987/88?

722 For which game was United's new West Stand used for the first time?

723 Against which club did United's keeper save two penalties in one match and who was the keeper?

724 Which former Magpie player was sent off three times in the season for his new club?

725 Who scored the winner in a 2-1 victory for a French side who visited Tyneside in February 1988?

726 Which two United men both scored and missed penalties in the season?

727 Which two players were sent off twice in the the season?

728 Who won several monthly awards, including five in a row, from Football League sponsors Barclays?

729 Brazilian International Mirandinha made one appearance for

United's reserve side during the season. Who were the opposition, and did he score?

730 In which match in the 1987/88 season did three Newcastle players reach personal milestones? One made his 100th League and Cup appearance for the club, another his 300th, and yet another reached 400 games in his career. Who are the three players?

UNITED GOALKEEPERS

731 Name three goalkeepers to have been capped at full level while at St James Park.

732 Who were United's keepers in the 1976 League Cup final and the 1952 FA Cup final?

733 This Magpie keeper made his debut at Leeds in 1970/71 and went on to appear in only 11 matches before signing for Darlington. Who is he?

734 Who is this? He was signed from Darlington in 1969 and made only one appearance before heading for Sheffield United.

735 Who was Newcastle's keeper in the 1924 FA Cup final?

736 A goalkeeper who played 107 times for United during the Thirties had the same name as a forward from the Seventies, and both at one time played for Preston. Who are the two players?

737 Which United goalkeeper signed for Carlisle United in 1985?

738 Gordon Lee signed a keeper from his old club in 1976. Who was he?

739 Who was the goalkeeper who started with United but never appeared in first-team football and later turned out for Derby County, Peterborough, Watford and Brighton?

740 Which Newcastle goalkeeper wrote, *Sure It's A Grand Old Team to Play For*?

MIXED BAG . . . 3

741 Which side equals United's 11 FA Cup final appearances?

742 Gates in excess of 40,000 have been recorded in testimonials for two of United's players. Name them.

743 On United's return to Division One in 1984/85 two players scored their first goal for the Magpies in the opening game against Leicester. Who were they?

744 True or False? United's biggest score in any fixture was a 21-1 victory on a tour of North America just after the War?

745 What game attracted 42,157, the best gate seen at St James Park since the visit of Sunderland in 1976?

746 Who was the United coach who later became manager of Sporting Lisbon?

747 Who is United's longest-serving captain with eight years service?

748 A past United player's father skippered a Wembley Cup final side in 1966. Who are the two players involved?

749 Name one ex-League club the Magpies have faced in post-war football.

750 Who was the PFA Young Player of the Year runner-up to Mark Hughes in 1985?

MIXED BAG . . . 4

751 Which ex-United player took part in England's defeat by the USA in the World Cup of 1950?

752 Who were the Magpies' opponents when they won the FA Youth Cup in 1962 and 1985?

753 Name the former Newcastle striker who was picked for the England non-League international squad in 1987/88?

754 Who holds the record for the shortest senior career with United after appearing in only 15 minutes of his debut v. Forest in 1959, before being carried off with an ankle injury, and never played for United again?

755 Which player was capped for Wales the day after playing for United's 'A' Team against Reyrolles?

756 Which Newcastle goalkeeper on his Football League debut lost 0-9 and on his Newcastle home debut lost 1-6?

757 This player became United's first substitute appearance and

also the first sub to score, in two different games. Who is he?

758 Name two English towns with the same name as a United player?

759 Why was United's match at Huddersfield in 1954 delayed by 25 minutes?

760 What was so special about Kenny Dalglish's goal for Liverpool against United in August 1977?

MIX-UP . . . 2

Rearrange the letters to find a United player:

761 R E Y R T / T E M O M R T D C
762 Y R G A / L K L Y E
763 I L O C N / G E T S U G T
764 E P R T E / E T W I H
765 L B I L / P E D A R A P L Y
766 E R G G O E / A N A N H H
767 M O T M Y / K E R A L W
768 M I A L / U T H O Y
769 N A A L / V A D E S I
770 R E T P E / D A Y R E B E L S

WELSH CONNECTION

771 Who was United's first Welsh International player?

772 Which United Welshman appeared against Hungary in 1986, his only honour with the Magpies?

773 Name two of the three Welsh international centre-forwards to have played for United?

774 One member of Newcastle's promotion side in 1965 later played for Wales. Who is he?

775 Name United's only current Welshman.

776 Which Welsh club have United faced in Cup football in the last ten years?

777 Which one of United's Welsh internationals was born in Chepstow, Gwent, in 1941?

778 Who was the last Welsh international outfield player to appear for United?

779 Three United players were capped by their country when regulars in United's reserve line-up. Name two of them.

780 Against which club did Welsh centre-forward Wyn Davies make his debut for United on 29 October 1966?

781 United nearly won "The Double" in season 1950/51. What position in the First Division did they finish?

782 Fifty League and Cup games were played in the season. Name two of the three players who appeared in all games.

783 United's forward line played in every game en route to Wembley in the FA Cup. Name it, from 7-11.

784 A famous defender made his debut against Middlesbrough at centre-forward, and he scored. Who was he?

785 United signed a new goalkeeper during the season. What was he called?

786 Which club defeated United 7-0 in the season?

787 The Magpies played four clubs starting with the initial 'B' on their Cup run. Name the clubs.

788 One player appeared for the Rest of UK side v. Wales during the year. Who was he?

789 Where did the black'n'whites play their two semi-final games against Wolves?

790 Which United star was known as "Pancho"?

AUTOGRAPHS

Whose autographs are these?

791

792

793

794

795

796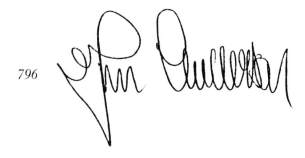

797 Frank Brennan

798

799

800

801 During the Twenties United met this famous amateur combination at Selhurst Park. What were they called?

802 Who is United's oldest medal winner at 41 years and 8 months old?

803 Which Welsh club, no longer in the Football League, did United defeat 4-1 at St James Park in the 3rd round in 1926?

804 In 1945/46, which club did United meet over two legs in the FA Cup 3rd round?

805 Who was that club's ace goalscorer and future United star?

806 In the last Cup-tie before the War, United fell to the Cup-holders 2-1 at Gallowgate. In the opponents' line-up was Bill Shankly. Who were the opposition?

807 United defeated this north-east club 4-1 in 1925, the only time the black'n'whites have faced them in senior football. Which club is it?

808 The club's biggest defeat at Gallowgate in the F A Cup was a 5-0 reverse in 1914. Which side inflicted the record?

809 United have played this southern club twice in semi-finals, both prior to World War Two. Name the club.

810 In the 1906 Cup run to the final, Newcastle conceded only one goal. Which club scored the goal?

MALCOLM MACDONALD

811 Malcolm Macdonald's family home was next to which football ground?

812 He started his career as a full-back with which non-League side?

813 What was the transfer fee Arsenal paid United for his services?

814 Which clubs has Malcolm Macdonald managed?

815 When did he win his first cap for England, and against which country?

816 Malcolm's debut for United was against which continental side? He scored in a 2-1 defeat.

817 When at Highbury, Supermac appeared on loan with a club in which European country?

818 After scoring five goals for England he jointly holds the country's scoring record this century. With which other player does he share the record and against which country did he net the five?

819 He also holds another England goals record. What is it?

820 What did Supermac arrive in at St James Park for his Press Call on signing for Luton?

821 Which club did United forward Peter Noble sign for in 1968?

822 Former Everton and Scotland striker Jim Pearson left Newcastle in 1980, for which ex-League club?

823 United star of Edwardian times Jock Rutherford left Tyneside in 1913, to which club?

824 Keith Kennedy, brother of Alan, left United in 1972. He went on to appear over 400 times for which club?

825 Welsh international forward Ken Leek stayed at St James Park for a matter of only six months. Which club did he join in 1961?

826 Mick Martin joined which club in September 1983 after five years as a Newcastle player?

827 In 1985 full-back Malcolm Brown departed after playing 45 games in a United shirt. Which club did he join?

828 Bobby Corbett appeared for United in the 1951 Cup final but was transferred to this club shortly afterwards. Name the side.

829 Wyn Davies played for several clubs after leaving United in 1971. Which club paid £52,500 for his services in that year?

830 Newcastle's Ian Davies also turned out for many clubs after his stay on Tyneside. He left in 1982, to which side?

PHOTOFIT . . . 3

831 Who are the two United players featured in this international work-out?

832 Who is this United schemer?

833 A young-looking Magpie hero in the Forties. Who is he?

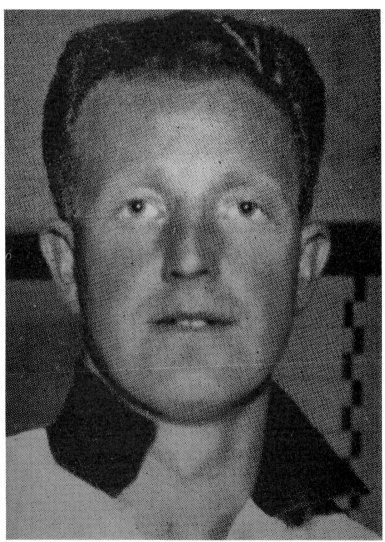

834 This player was capped many times for his country. Who?

835 Who is this Newcastle forward?

836 A Seventies defender. What is his name?

837 A Newcastle number 9. Who?

838 Destined for England, some said. Who is he?

839 A Scot with a real Scots name. Who?

840 Pictured in Blackpool colours. Who is he?

841 Who missed United's penalties in the shoot-out against Pesci Dosza in the Fairs Cup of 1971?

842 In season 1973/74 which club did United face seven times in the one season, six of the games in a six-week spell?

843 United lost 9-1 to Nottingham Forest during the Eighties. What was the tournament called?

844 Name three of the four top-of-the-bill rock-star attractions to be seen at St James Park latterly.

845 Which two clubs took part in the FA Amateur Cup final replay at Gallowgate in 1954 before a 56,000 crowd?

846 United faced two clubs in the Coronation Cup of 1953 in Glasgow. Which sides were they?

847 Who succeeded Joe Harvey as captain in 1953?

848 On how many occasions in Cup finals did United play at the old Edwardian Crystal Palace stadium, and did they ever win there?

849 Name one of the two Scottish clubs United attempted to take the place of in 1932 with their reserve side.

850 Newcastle had a Portuguese goalkeeper on their books for six months in 1978/79. Who was he?

851 Who was the Maltese International on trial with United in November and December 1977, later to play in the European Cup?

852 United full-back Ron Guthrie holds a rare distinction. What?

853 Two Newcastle managers have appeared in World Cup finals as players. Who are they?

854 Which three clubs have United faced twice in major Cup finals?

855 When Sunderland defeated United 9-1 at Gallowgate in 1908/09, what was the score at half-time?

856 Who scored United's goal from the penalty spot on his home debut in that fixture?

857 In 1959 the Magpies recorded a 8-2 win over which Lancashire club?

858 United defeated the reigning League Champions 7-2 in season 1951/52. Who were the title-holders?

859 What was the reason for the postponement of the visit of Liverpool to Tyneside in December 1974?

860 United have faced one non-League side in the FA Cup semi-final prior to World War One. Which side was it? They much later won the Football League Cup.

JACKIE MILBURN

861 In what year did Jackie Milburn first play for United?

862 In what capacity did Jackie leave and join Linfield in 1957?

863 He managed two clubs in England, one League, one non-League. Name them.

864 What do his famous Christian name initials, JET, stand for?

865 What was extra special about his goal in the 1955 Cup final?

866 Apart from Jackie and Bobby Charlton, name two other footballing members of his family, including their League side.

867 Did Jackie Milburn appear in the number 9 shirt in each of United's Cup finals of the Fifties?

868 When did he first appear in the centre-forward position for the Magpies? Was it in 1945, 1947 or 1950?

869 What happened on that day?

870 Against which country, in 1949, did Jackie win the first of his 13 England caps?

Jackie Milburn, a Tyneside legend

871 On what special day of the year did United clinch promotion with a victory over Bolton Wanderers?

872 United made only one signing in the transfer market, in February. Who did they sign for £10,000 from Chelsea?

873 Newcastle defeated this club 6-1 away from Tyneside, one of the side's best away victories ever. Who were the opposition?

874 This player scored three of the four goals which defeated Middlesbrough twice in the space of two days at Xmas. Name him.

875 Who was the Magpies' captain that season?

876 United lost only one home game, a controversial 3-2 defeat with a late goal in injury time. Which club defeated United?

877 Against Bolton in the clinching promotion fixture, the visitors possessed two players who caused United problems. Both became famous internationals, and both for a spell at Maine Road. Who are they?

878 Five players were ever-presents in the promotion side. Can you name three?

879 Who was the side's top scorer with 16 goals?

880 Who was United's vice-captain in the year?

881 Who is this Scot? At James Park briefly in 1980, a big-money buy from Scotland for both Arsenal and Villa.

882 Which former United favourite became Scottish Footballer of the Year in 1967?

883 Which Newcastle international Scottish centre-forward found further fame in the confectionery business?

884 Name two Scots post-war captains to have played for United to the end of 1987/88 season.

885 Name three Scots to have appeared for United in the last five years (to 1987/88 season).

886 Which ex-United player has appeared in the World Cup finals for the Scots?

887 Name two of United's centre-forwards to be born at Bellshill in Lanark.

888 Who was the Scot to arrive at Gallowgate after an exchange for Ralph Callachan in 1978?

889 Who is this United Scot? His previous clubs include Muirhead, Glasgow Pollock, Jordanhill, and his brother was in the same side for a now defunct Scots League outfit.

890 Which Scottish club did United defeat 9-2 in 1960?

SAME NAMES . . . 3

891 JIM & DAVE . . . . : At St James Park together in 1970, one a player, one a coach

892 IAN & JIMMY . . . . : One a World Cup player, the other a film-star namesake.

893 COLIN & ERNIE . . . . : Two post-war favourites, one a winger, the other quite a schemer.

894 MARTIN & BARRIE . . . . : 50 goals for one, no goals for the other.

895 GEORGE & WILLIE . . . . : Both to lift silverware, and both pre-war stars.

896 ALBERT & TOM . . . . : Two from Scotland, two midfielders.

897 MATT & JAMES . . . . : Two more from north of the border with the ideal name.

898 JACK & GEOFF . . . . : A couple of forwards, one a Wembley King.

899 JOHN & STAN . . . . : Solid International men.

900 COLIN & JIMMY . . . . : Two dashing pre-1960 forwards.

901 Who is this Newcastle post-war goalpoacher?

902 A United forward in Charlie Mitten's continental strip.
Name him.

903 Pictured is a United full-back challenging a former Newcastle winger. Can you name both players?

904 Who are these happy Magpies, and what is the trophy?

905 Goalmouth action from 1965. Who is the United forward, who is the goalkeeper (a former Newcastle man) and who are the opposition?

906 Name the two players challenging for the ball at St James Park.

907 A United centre-forward, but who?

908 The "Blue Star" is featured prominently on this player's shirt. Who is he?

909 A Fifties favourite. Can you recognise him?

910 An early shot of a Magpie player, in his previous club's colours. Who is he and which team's colours are they?

911 Who was the last forward to hit 30 goals in a single season for United?

912 Who wrote *Win!*?

913 Which latter-day United player was capped for England v. Iceland with his previous club in 1981/82?

914 Which recent Newcastle striker played for Mexborough?

915 Who was known as "Cassius"?

916 Which Magpie centre-forward holds Scunthorpe United's scoring record?

917 Who scored the black'n'whites' first goal in the promotion-winning clash over Bolton Wanderers in 1965?

918 Which United striker made his Football League debut with United when aged 25, straight from non-League soccer?

919 A Newcastle forward of the late Sixties possessed the initials JEWS. Who was he?

920 Two famous United centre-forwards had spells with South African club Arcadia Shepherds. One was Peter Withe, who was the other?

921 Which United player of the last 20 years amassed the following honours; Football League Championship, Football League Division Two Championship, FA Cup finalist, Football League Cup Winners, European Cup Winners, Inter Cities Fairs Cup Winners, FA Amateur Cup Winners and Football League side?

922 Which two United Greats regularly sit on the Pools Panel?

923 Which Newcastle player signed for United twice: in January 1973 and again in September 1982?

924 Which Magpie forward appeared for England in 1940 and then Scotland in 1947?

925 Was he English or Scottish?

926 This player scored on his debut in December 1969 v. Ipswich. He was swopped for Jackie Sinclair and later

swopped again, this time for John Tudor. Name him.

927 Which one of United's Wembley stars holds a degree in Economics?

928 Who holds the record for the shortest stay at the club?

929 Three ex-United men won Football League Cup Winner's medals with a Third Division side. Name all three men.

930 Which United skipper was later the manager of Bradford and Cardiff City?

JOE HARVEY

931 Where was Joe Harvey born?

932 Joe played Football League soccer for one other club. Name the club.

933 He captained the Football League XI in 1951. True or False?

934 In which Cup finals did Joe lead United out at Wembley?

935 Joe was also coach to a north-east amateur side after leaving United. What was the name of the club?

936 When did he rejoin the Magpies as manager?

937 Which was Harvey's last season in charge at Gallowgate?

938 His birthday in 1969 was an extra special occasion. Why?

939 During the war Joe guested for two Scottish clubs. Name one of them.

940 Joe was in the Royal Artillery during the War. What rank did he hold?

United's long–serving Yorkshireman, Joe Harvey

941   Who scored a goal in his first two games for United in season 1968/69, both four-goal away wins?

942   Jack Charlton was in charge of United for only one year. What season was it?

943   On tour of South Africa in 1952 United defeated Border Province 10-0. Who scored seven goals in that game?

944   In which city did United meet Brazilians Pele and Santos in 1972?

945   The Magpies have faced three Russian sides at St James Park. Name two of the clubs.

946   Who did the black'n'whites face in Willie McFaul's testimonial match in 1979?

947   Which Brazilian side did United meet at Gallowgate in 1974/75?

948   Which Heaton lad and ex-United forward played for the Washington Diplomats?

949   Two clubs were promoted with Newcastle in season 1983/84. Name them.

950   Which two brothers, in a United match and on opposing sides, scored in February 1973?

FIRST NAMES . . . 2

951   – – – – – – – / BROWN : Went back to his previous club.

952   – – – – – – / FRANKS : Throw-in expert.

953   – – – – – / JOHNSON : To Tees-side.

954   – – – – – – – / SPENCER : England defender.

955   – – – – – / SMITH : European coach.

SECOND NAMES . . . 2

956   KEITH / – – – – – – – – – – – – : Midfielder.

957   BRIAN / – – – – – – : Famous name.

958   TOMMY / – – – – – – – – : Assistant boss.

959 CHARLIE / − − − − − − : Netted over 250 goals.
960 JOHN / − − − − − − − : Cast-iron defender from Scotland.

961 Who said, "I told him not to be such a big baby"?
962 United have drawn two games by the scoreline of 5-5, both against London opposition. Name the clubs.
963 Three of United's England men were capped at centre-forward. Who are they?
964 Which French club did the Magpies play in the Festival of Britain celebration match in 1950/51?
965 Who said, "People keep on talking about stars and flair. As far as I'm concerned you find stars in the sky and flair is something on the bottom of trousers"?
966 Name the two players to be carried off the Wembley pitch in Newcastle's 1950s FA Cup finals, and name the clubs they played for.
967 In 1949 United played ten games on tour and won all ten scoring 79 goals. But which country did they visit?
968 What did United and their supporters win in 1970?
969 Who captained Scotland's Under-23 side in 1974/75?
970 Who said, "I've heard of players selling dummies, but this club keeps buying them."?

971 Who was United's skipper from 1965 to 1968?
972 Which four sides did United play en route to winning the Japan Cup in 1983?
973 Which Magpie striker holds the record for netting the greatest number of penalties in a season for United?
974 Who scored what is thought to be the fastest own-goal at St James Park after only 20 seconds of United's fixture with Ipswich Town?
975 Len White and Arthur Bottom scored five goals each in a

friendly match in 1958. United won 12-1. Who were the opposition?

976 In 1927 when the Magpies last won the title, which club did the black'n'whites beat to the Championship? Was it Liverpool, Sunderland or Huddersfield Town?

977 United once drew 6-6 with Gateshead before a 15,000 crowd at St James Park. True or False?

978 Who won United's supporters' Golden Boot Award with 32 goals in 1981?

979 Which post-war Newcastle goalkeeper has scored a goal in a first-class game for United?

980 Name two ex-players since the War that have ended up as United senior coach.

FA CUP TEASERS

981 What was unusual about United's home tie with Manchester City in 1975?

982 United have played FA Cup football only once on a Sunday, in 1985. Who were the opposition and what was the scoreline?

983 Which club have the black'n'whites opposed the most in FA Cup football? Is it Sheffield Wednesday, Nottingham Forest, Tottenham Hotspur or Everton?

984 United have conceded only five goals in semi-final games. Who defeated United in 1947 by 4-0?

985 In 1988, 1969, 1954, 1947 and 1960 Newcastle were beaten by the eventual Cup winners. Name three of the four victors.

986 Since the War Newcastle have drawn four non-League sides in the Cup. Name them.

987 Which three players appeared in all three Fifties FA Cup finals?

988 In which year did United field the same 11 players all the way to Wembley?

989 Which two clubs have lifted the Cup more than United's six wins?

990 Which club did United play at Elland Road in 1976, this after two drawn games? And what was the final result?

991 Who was Percy Harper and why does he play an important part in United's inter-war history?

992 Which German side did United meet on their North American tour in 1970?

993 Who is Newcastle's longest-serving Director?

994 Which post-war United boss was famed for his singing and sculpting?

995 A member of United's backroom staff turned out for the Magpies against the Isle of Man XI in 1986. Who was he?

996 Which ex-United forward wrote, *Going for Goal*?

997 Since the double centre-half game materialised in 1966, only once have United's twin central defenders both scored in the same match. The game was against Manchester City in 1986. Who scored?

998 In 1957 a Wembley Cup final contained two ex-United reserve players, both never playing League or Cup football for the Magpies. Who were the players and the sides they represented at Wembley?

999 "Daddler" was a nickname from days of old. Who did it belong to?

1000 Who handed out calling-cards entitled "Have Goals Will Travel" after a TV series?

1001 Name the three Magpie goalgetters to score the 81 goals, and form United's best forward partnership, when the club won the title in 1927.

1002 Who became the first man to play for and manage winning Cup final sides?

1003 Who captained the black'n'whites' FA Youth Cup winning side in 1962?

1004 What was the name of Newcastle's mascot dog during the 1900s?

1005 Who supposedly gave the nickname of the Magpies to United?

1006 Only one boss has won two Manager of the Month Awards with Newcastle. Who was he?

1007 Who topped the season's Second Division goalscoring list in 1946/47 with 30 goals for United?

1008 A Finnish international defender appeared in several friendly games in 1980 but never signed for the club on a permanent basis. Name him.

1009 Who presented the FA Cup to skipper Joe Harvey in 1952?

1010 What was the name of Inter Milan's goalkeeper sent off during a Fairs Cup match at Gallowgate in 1970?

STOPPAGE TIME

1011 A former Newcastle player is the oldest man to score in a League Cup final. Who is he?

1012 Which Mayor of Wolverhampton was a former United winger?

1013 Joe Harvey and Keith Burkinshaw were manager and coach at St James Park. They were also together as boss and player at which other club?

1014 Which famous goalkeeper made his 1,000th appearance against United?

1015 Which United player was signed twice by the club, once as an outside-left, and then again as goalkeeper?

1016 Which club sent their first-team to play United's reserve side in a Central League fixture in 1972?

1017 The FA Cup-tie in 1950 with Chelsea saw both trainers with the same Christian and surname. Both were Geordies, but not related. Who were they?

1018 Which United captain was sent off for his country against Bulgaria in 1977? One of a few players sent off in an international fixture.

1019 What was significant about United's playing squad in 1982/83?

1020 Who was the former United player in charge of Leeds City when they were kicked out of the Football League in 1919?

Answers

1   Michael O'Neill
2   Southampton
3   Manchester United. He scored both goals in a 2-2 draw.
4   Blackpool and Wimbledon
5   Anth Lormor
6   Arthur Cox with Derby County
7   Lee Clark (Under-15) and Stephen Didlick (Under-18)
8   Shrewsbury Town in the Simod Cup
9   Chelsea
10   Cappielow Park, home of Greenock Morton

RECENT EVENTS . . . I

11   United went top of Division One for the first time in 34 years after beating Villa 3-0.
12   P Beardsley, N McDonald, J Wrightson, A Lormor
13   K Scott, G Kelly, P Jackson, J Wrightson, B Tinnion
14   David McCreery
15   George Reilly
16   Everton (1986/87)
17   Mick Harford
18   Three home defeats from the start of the season
19   Glyn Hodges (from Wimbledon)
20   Willie McFaul (Keegan's match was not a testimonial)

CURRENT STARS

21   Neil McDonald
22   Glenn Roeder
23   Martin Thomas
24   Glenn V Roeder
25   Roeder, Cornwell, Goddard
26   1974/75
27   Martin Thomas

28 Kenny Wharton
29 Paul Stephenson
30 Darren Jackson

CLUB FACTS ... I

31 1904/05, 1906/07, 1908/09, 1926/27
32 December 1892
33 1952 v. Arsenal (1-0)
34 1882 as Newcastle East End
35 1962 & 1985
36 1964/65
37 1947 v. Charlton
38 1909
39 False, they were knocked out at the semi-final stage
40 1948

CLUB FIRSTS

41 1910
42 True
43 Feyenoord, a 4-0 victory
44 Barcelona
45 Malcolm Macdonald (v. Doncaster 1973)
46 Ollie Burton
47 Dave Hollins
48 Jimmy Smith (from Aberdeen)
49 1924
50 Denmark

WHO'S WHO ... I

51 David Craig
52 Stuart Barrowclough
53 Benny Craig

54 Hughie Gallacher
55 Peter Jackson
56 Terry Hibbitt
57 Alan Kennedy
58 Alf McMichael
59 Mick Martin
60 Bob Stokoe

PAUL GASGOIGNE

61 Dunston, Gateshead
62 1967
63 Redheugh Boys' Club
64 QPR
65 Oxford United 1985/86
66 False
67 Morocco
68 Watford
69 Tottenham, Swindon Town
70 QPR, Derby County

UNITED IN THE FA CUP . . . THE EIGHTIES

71 Luton Town
72 John Brownlie, Wes Saunders
73 Liverpool (1983/84), Exeter City (1980/81)
74 Gary Megson v. Nottingham Forest
75 Swindon Town (1987/88)
76 Brighton (1985/86, 1982/83)
77 John McGrath, manager of Preston
78 Northampton (1987)
79 K Carr, M Thomas, G Kelly
80 Chris Waddle

UNITED MASTERMIND . . . 1

81 Irving Nattrass (with 22 games)

82 C Veitch, J Rutherford, J Lawrence
83 S Seymour (Newcastle 1924, 51, 52), P McWilliam (Newcastle 1910, Spurs 1921), R Stokoe (Newcastle 1955, Sunderland 1973)
84 I Bogie (1983), N McDonald (1981), D McClean (1973), J Trewick (1972), C Guthrie (1969)
85 v. Swansea FAC 1953 (fog), v. Forest FAC 1974 (crowd trouble)
86 Burnley, Stoke, Blackburn Rovers
87 Ray Bowden
88 Real Madrid
89 Manchester City
90 United won with a full reserve side, just prior to the FA Cup final

UNITED MIX

91 Glenn Roeder (with QPR)
92 Ron Batty
93 Ron Batty
94 Trevor Hockey
95 Everton
96 Birmingham
97 H Gallacher, W Appleyard, B Cairns, B Blanthorne
98 Chris Waddle
99 Jackie Charlton
100 Jim Barron, David Lawson

UNITED STRIKERS...I

101 I Broadis (1954), P Beardsley (1986), G Robledo (1950)
102 Alan Brown (of Sunderland)
103 Andy Parkinson
104 Micky Burns
105 Ray Clarke
106 Bobby Cummings
107 Keith Dyson

108 Jack Allen

109 Albert Stubbins

110 Billy Foulkes

PICTURE QUIZ ... I

111 Kenny Wharton

112 Peter Johnson

113 Colin Suggett

114 John Brownlie

115 Chris Withe

116 Peter Cartwright

117 Graham Oates

118 Aiden McCaffery

119 A Kennedy, F Clark, G Nulty, M Mahoney

120 Gary Nicholson

INTERNATIONAL MAGPIES ... I

121 P Beardsley, M Macdonald, J Milburn, C Waddle and I Broadis

122 Alf McMichael (for N Ireland)

123 Bob Moncur & Andy Aitken

124 T Cassidy, D Craig, W McFaul, O Burton, T Green, R Moncur, M Macdonald

125 P Arentoft (Denmark), G Robledo (Chile), Mirandinha (Brazil), F Koenen (Holland Under-21)

126 M Macdonald, J Milburn, L White

127 Mirandinha, J Anderson, P Goddard, D McCreery, M O'Neill, M Thomas

128 True. Alan appeared for the England "B" side in 1978 before his transfer to Liverpool.

129 Bill Curry

130 All former Youth Internationals.

DATES ... I

131 Jackie Milburn's last game for United

140

132 v. Bastia, United's last European game with J Rep of Holland scoring two goals

133 Last full International fixture at St James Park. England v. Norway

134 v. Palace. Debuts for M Macdonald and T Hibbitt

135 v. Liverpool. Kevin Keegan's farewell match

136 v. Feyenoord. United's debut in Europe

137 v. Everton. H Gallacher's debut against D Dean of Everton

138 v. Liverpool. M Macdonald's League debut at St James Park netting a hat-trick

139 Jackie Milburn's testimonial match

140 Blyth Spartans v. Wrexham FA Cup replay at St James Park

UNITED IN THE EIGHTIES . . . I

141 Sunderland

142 Alan Shoulder

143 Chris Waddle

144 I Varadi, K Keegan, P Beardsley, C Waddle, M O'Neill

145 T McDermott, C Waddle

146 Ian Baird

147 P Beardsley, D McCreery, I Stewart

148 M Thomas, C Hedworth, P Beardsley

149 Billy Whitehurst

150 West Ham United

SCOTS CONNECTION . . . I

151 J Blackley, J Brownlie, R Moncur, F Brennan, J Scoular

152 B Mitchell, T Pearson, J Connolly, A Cropley, J Scott, J Sinclair, M McGhee

153 T Craig, T Green, J Smith

154 Bob Moncur

155 All scored on their debut for Scotland

156 D Jackson, A Craig, A Gourley

157 Hughie Gallacher (1929)

158 A Cunningham, G Martin, D Livingstone
159 Manager John Blackley and assistant John Brownlie
160 Ayr United

MIX-UP . . . I

161 Paul Goddard
162 Frank Brennan
163 Terry Hibbitt
164 John Craggs
165 Paul Stephenson
166 Kevin Keegan
167 Franz Koenen
168 Ronnie Simpson
169 Darren Jackson
170 Colin Veitch

EARLY HISTORY

171 Stanley and Rosewood
172 Bath Lane Hall, Newcastle
173 Woolwich Arsenal, Rotherham Town, Liverpool
174 Kaffirs
175 Fielding weak teams in League games prior to the FA Cup final
176 North Eastern League
177 1933
178 J Sorley and T Crate
179 R Aitken, R Kelso
180 Burton Wanderers

FOOTBALL LEAGUE CHAMPIONS

181 1926/27
182 F Hudspeth and H Gallacher

183 Hughie Gallacher
184 1951 (4th)
185 1984/85 (during September)
186 United recorded their heaviest home defeat, 1-9 to Sunderland
187 Aston Villa
188 Unbeaten at home, United lost to non-League Crystal Palace in the FA Cup at St James Park
189 Everton. They were 2nd, 3rd and 2nd when United won the title.
190 John Bailey (1985 with Everton)

MAGPIE ASSORTMENT ... I

191 Albert Stubbins
192 Ernie Taylor (Newcastle, Blackpool and Manchester United)
193 Chris R Waddle
194 Jack Charlton
195 Keith Burkinshaw
196 J Harvey, G Lee, R Dinnis, B McGarry, A Cox, J Charlton
197 Lord Westwood (1974-81)
198 True (on 18 April 1903)
199 1938 v. Norway
200 Tommy Craig

PETER BEARDSLEY

201 v. Barnsley, in the number 12 shirt (1983/84)
202 Gillingham, Cambridge United, Burnley and Newcastle United
203 Vancouver Whitecaps
204 One (a Milk Cup-tie v. Bournemouth as sub)
205 Alan Davies
206 Egypt

207 Mexico

208 Andrew

209 £120,000

210 Bill McGarry

UNITED DEFENDERS

211 John Bird

212 Stuart Boam

213 Malcolm Brown

214 Jesse Carver

215 Bruce Halliday

216 George Heslop (with Manchester City)

217 Frank Clark

218 Frank Brennan

219 Jeff Clarke

220 Wes Saunders

REMEMBER SEASON ... 1982/83

221 C Waddle and I Varadi

222 Rotherham (5-1), Barnsley (5-0)

223 T McDermott and M Channon

224 Leeds United

225 Howard Gayle from Liverpool

226 N McDonald, P Ferris

227 United ended up with only nine men, Carney and McDermott being sent off

228 QPR, Wolves and Leicester City

229 J Clarke (Sunderland), S Carney (Blyth Spartans)

230 Trelford Mills, the referee who disallowed two goals v. Brighton

PICTURE QUIZ ... 2

231 Viv Busby

232 Ian Mitchell

233 James Rush

234 Keith Robson
235 Tommy Walker
236 Keith Burkinshaw
237 Tom Mather
238 Bob Stokoe
239 Tommy Thompson
240 Tommy Knox

THE MEN IN CHARGE

241 A Cunningham (in 1929, he was aged 38 when appointed player-boss)
242 A Cunningham (1932), S Seymour (1951, 1952), D Livingstone (1955), J Harvey (1974), G Lee (1976), W McFaul (1988)
243 A Cunningham, C Mitten, B McGarry
244 W McFaul, J Harvey, S Seymour, A Cunningham
245 Charlie Mitten. He picked his son John and nephew Albert Scanlon
246 False. Harvey gained promotion from Division Two in 1965.
247 Gordon Lee
248 Bill McGarry
249 A Cunningham (Scotland), J Charlton (England), W McFaul (Ireland), B McGarry (England)
250 Coventry City as a player, and Chesterfield as a manager

UNITED IN THE LEAGUE CUP

251 Colchester United
252 Sunderland. United lost after a penalty shoot-out
253 2-7 v. Manchester United
254 Oxford United (1983/84 and 1985/86)
255 Alan Gowling
256 It was an own-goal by County keeper McManus, direct from a long throw by Macdonald
257 Alan Suddick and Micky Burns
258 Arsenal
259 Peter Cartwright

260 Jim Iley

UNITED MASTERMIND . . . 2

261 United scored all six goals, Harvey and Brennan netting own-goals
262 Northampton Town
263 Everton, Tottenham, Manchester United, Chelsea
264 Every member of United's side, including the goalkeeper, scored
265 Jackie Milburn in 1951
266 M Macdonald (1974), W Appleyard (1908), A Shepherd (1911)
267 Derby County
268 Aldershot, Darlington, Mansfield Town, Rochdale, Southend United, Scarborough
269 All played for United during World War Two
270 Roma, Bologna, Como, Torino, Fiorentina

WHERE DID THEY COME FROM?

271 Hamilton Accies
272 Everton
273 Manchester United
274 Bradford Park Avenue
275 Dundee United
276 Torquay United
277 Linfield
278 Clydebank
279 Chesterfield
280 Leeds United and Birmingham City

UNITED IN THE FA CUP . . . THE SEVENTIES

281 Derby County (1976)

282 1973/74 (Forest), 1975/76 (Derby County)
283 Ian Mitchell
284 Brendan Forster
285 Chester (1979/80), Wrexham (1977/78), Walsall (1974/75)
286 Elland Road, Leeds
287 Manchester City
288 After the Manchester City tie, manager Gordon Lee joined Everton
289 Stuart Robinson
290 Wembley, Hillsborough, Goodison Park, Vicarage Road

AUTOGRAPHS . . . I

291 Ivor Allchurch
292 Jack Charlton
293 Mirandinha
294 Bob Moncur
295 Neil McDonald
296 Jackie Milburn
297 Preban Arentoft
298 Charlie Mitten
299 Glenn Roeder
300 Ted Robledo

RECENT STARS

301 Paul Goddard
302 Tony Nesbit
303 Alan Kennedy
304 John Trewick and Peter Withe
305 Steve Hardwick
306 Mick Channon
307 Jeff Wrightson
308 Darren Jackson
309 Alan Davies and Joe Allon
310 Peter Haddock

MAGPIE ASSORTMENT . . . 2

311 SEC Bastia (1977)
312 David, Tom, Derek, Albert, Ben . . . CRAIG
313 Charlie Mitten
314 Peter Beardsley
315 1971/72
316 Bohemians (1977 UEFA Cup)
317 J Clarke, R Moncur, T Gibb, B Robson
318 J Sinclair, T Hibbitt, T Craig
319 Jim Pearson
320 P Beardsley, C Waddle, M Harford

LOOSE ENDS . . . 1

321 George Robledo
322 R Moncur and D Craig
323 Willie McFaul
324 Bobby and Jackie Charlton
325 Terry Hibbitt
326 Jimmy Smith (v. Birmingham City Texaco Cup)
327 Mick Martin (Eire), David McCreery (N Ireland)
328 Alan Gowling
329 George Reilly
330 All red

SAME NAMES . . . 1

331 R Blackhall, J Blyth
332 J Denmark
333 L White, A or M Brown, T Green, T Grey
334 A Bottom, A Shoulder, G Hair
335 T Hockey
336 D or P Jackson, A or K Kennedy, D Ford, E Taylor,
P Johnson, Wilson
337 MacDonald (several), Wilson (several), Russell, Grey

338 L Shackleton
339 J Nelson, A Bruce, J Gordon, J Tudor, G Moses
340 D Ford, R Bentley

UNITED MIDFIELD MEN

341 Graham Oates
342 John Cowan
343 Tommy Craig
344 Alan Suddick
345 Keith Kettleborough
346 Pat Heard
347 Tom Curry
348 Ray Hudson
349 Duncan Neale (v. Fulham 1961)
350 George Eastham

PICTURE QUIZ . . . 3

351 Ken Leek
352 Dave Hollins
353 Keith Kennedy
354 Alan Kirkman
355 Billy Foulkes
356 Alex Reid
357 Ronnie Simpson and Dick Keith
358 Ian Davies
359 P Howard, M Macdonald, M Mahoney, S Barrowclough, A
     Gowling, G Keeley, R Blackhall, T Cassidy, G Nulty, I
     Nattrass, P Cannell
360 John Connolly

MAGPIES IN EUROPE

361 1968/69

362 Vittoria Setubal, Sporting Lisbon
363 1-3 v. SEC Bastia
364 Jim Scott and Jackie Sinclair
365 F Clark, W Davies, T Gibb, W McFaul, B Robson, J Scott
366 Feyenoord (1968, as sub)
367 Dundee United, Southampton
368 Inter Milan
369 Ujpest Dosza, Pesci Dosza
370 Real Zaragoza, Southampton

NICKNAMES . . . I

371 "Bones"
372 Tommy Gibb
373 Bryan Robson
374 Bobby Mitchell
375 "Ankles"
376 Alwyn Burton
377 Jock Rutherford
378 Peter McWilliam
379 M Macdonald, W Davies
380 Wilf Low

ST JAMES PARK

381 1972/73
382 The Freemen of the City of Newcastle
383 1905
384 1978
385 S African rugby team
386 Glasgow Celtic
387 1983
388 Monaco 1987/88
389 Bishop Auckland v. Crook Town
390 Harlem Globetrotters

MIXED BAG . . . 1

391 Swansea (A)
392 Barnsley
393 Middlesbrough
394 True (in 1933)
395 1944/45
396 Orient and Ipswich Town
397 Crystal Palace. Malcolm Macdonald netted three
398 West Ham United, 1-8
399 True. United have not won at Cambridge United, Newport
      Co. or Shrewsbury Town
400 Newcastle United v. Manchester City, Football League Cup
      final 1976

MIXED BAG . . . 2

401 John Anderson and Steve Doyle (now Sunderland)
402 Stan Anderson
403 Benny Arentoft
404 Tommy Cassidy
405 Wyn, Reg, Alan . . . DAVIES
406 Tommy Gibb
407 Mick Channon
408 F Clark (Orient), J McGrath (PNE), W McFaul (Newcastle
      United), J Bird (Hartlepool), L Walker (Aldershot)
409 Paul Gascoigne
410 True, in season 1893/94

WHO'S WHO AND WHERE FROM

411 Geoff Nulty from Burnley
412 Billy Rafferty from Wolves
413 David McCreery from Tulsa Roughnecks
414 Albert McInroy from Sunderland
415 John Tudor from Sheffield United (alongside M Macdonald)

416 Sammy Weaver from Hull City
417 Gary Megson from Forest
418 Vic Keeble from Colchester United
419 John Bailey from Everton
420 David Mills from Sheffield Wednesday

WHO'S WHO AND WHERE TO

421 Len White to Huddersfield Town
422 Nigel Walker to San Diego
423 John Trewick to Oxford United
424 Bobby Shinton to Millwall
425 Ronnie Simpson to Hibernian
426 George Reilly to West Bromwich Albion
427 Mark McGhee to Aberdeen
428 Aiden McCaffrey to Derby County
429 Jeff Clarke to Ankara (Turkey)
430 Tony Cunningham to Blackpool

STAN SEYMOUR

431 1920/21
432 Kelloe, County Durham
433 FA Cup (1924), Football League Championship (1927)
434 Yes, an unofficial cap v. Australia
435 1938
436 False
437 19 goals
438 1951 and 1952
439 True. Three appearances
440 "Mr Newcastle"

UNITED IN THE FA CUP . . . THE SIXTIES

441 Fulham, Stockport Co., Stoke City, Sheffield United

442 Bradford City 6-1
443 Southampton
444 1964 and non-League Bedford Town
445 Manchester City
446 Carlisle United, Ollie Burton missed the penalty
447 Duncan Neale, Wyn Davies
448 Nottingham Forest
449 Sheffield Wednesday (1966)
450 Roy Bentley of Reading

PICTURE QUIZ . . . 4

451 George Robledo v. Stoke City
452 Micky Burns v. Leeds United
453 Alan Suddick v. Sunderland
454 The Baseball Ground, Derby. Alan Gowling scores
455 Peter Noble v. Fulham. Ron McGarry and Bryan Robson
456 Gordon Hughes v. Luton Town
457 Ivor Allchurch and Len White
458 Peter McWilliam
459 Billy Rafferty
460 Left-right: T Hibbitt, J Tudor, A Kennedy, J Smith, D
     Craig, T Cassidy, F Clark. They are celebrating victory in
     the FA Cup semi-final at Hillsborough

IRISH CONNECTION

461 J Anderson, G Kelly (of Irish parents), D McCreery, M
     O'Neill
462 Linfield
463 J Milburn, A McMichael, G Hannah, D Keith
464 Eric Ross
465 T Casey, D Keith, A McMichael
466 Mick Martin
467 Bill McCracken, 19 years
468 Tom Casey (George Hannah is English)

469 Frank Houghton

470 B McCracken, A McMichael, D Craig

FIRST NAMES . . . I

471 Ian DAVIES

472 Eddie EDGAR

473 Geoff ALLEN

474 Stan ANDERSON

475 Keith ROBSON

SECOND NAMES . . . I

476 Chris WITHE

477 John BLACKLEY

478 George EASTHAM

479 Andy THOMAS

480 Michael O'NEILL

SAME NAMES . . . 2

481 Crosson

482 Martin

483 Curry

484 Ferguson

485 Harvey

486 Hill

487 Kelly

488 Mitchell

489 Robson

490 Mills

UNITED'S BACKROOM BOYS

491 Yes (v. St Johnstone, February 1964)

492 J Q McPherson
493 Jimmy Greenhalgh
494 Keith Burkinshaw
495 Graham McDonnell
496 S Seymour, J Auld, R Bennie
497 Norman Smith
498 Ron Lewin
499 Lord Westwood
500 Frank Watt

HALF-TIME

501 Stockport Co (v. Halifax, 1934)
502 Arsenal (v. Blackpool, 1952/53)
503 Peter Noble (of Burnley)
504 Charlie Mitten
505 Albert Scanlon
506 Len Shackleton (v. Newport County)
507 First ever floodlit League game
508 Only League game without a corner
509 Youngest ever United team, aged an average 22 years 229
     days
510 Sheffield Wednesday

UNITED MASTERMIND . . . 3

511 A Aitken, J Howie, A McCombie, P McWilliam
512 Jackie Bell
513 Ray Bowden and Ralph Birkett
514 Bob Blanthorne
515 Frank Brennan (1969)
516 Ivor Broadis
517 Jock Wallace
518 George Dalton
519 Roy Bentley
520 Jimmy Gordon

UNITED MASTERMIND . . . 4

521 Martin Gorry
522 R Simpson, A Gowling
523 Harry Hardinge
524 Chris Harker (Bury)
525 Malcom Macdonald
526 Kenny Mitchell
527 John Mitten
528 Jimmy Thomson
529 Dixie Dean
530 Mick Martin

CLUB CONNECTIONS . . . 1

531 Jock Rutherford
532 Gordon Lee
533 Les O'Neil
534 Ron Greener
535 United's first game on *Match of the Day*
536 Andy Graver
537 P Withe, T Craig
538 Arthur Bottom
539 United fielded their oldest-ever side, average age 32 years 193 days
540 Fernando Varadi, brother of Imre

CLUB CONNECTIONS . . . 2

541 Kit Napier
542 John Pickering
543 Jackie Bell
544 City were relegated (They needed a point to survive but lost 3-2)
545 S Boam, G Nicholson, G Allen (coach)
546 Jock Rutherford
547 G Roeder, D McCreery, P Goddard, I Stewart

548 John McGrath
549 Tommy Robson
550 Reg, Ian, Alan DAVIES

UNITED IN THE EIGHTIES . . . 2

551 Terry McDermott
552 Bobby Shinton (7), Alan Shoulder (6)
553 P Beardsley, D McCreery, H Gayle, M Martin, S Hardwick
554 England Under-21 v. Hungary Under-21
555 Shrewsbury Town (1987/88)
556 Wimbledon
557 Glenn Roeder
558 Michael O'Neill
559 George Best (for Hibernian)
560 J Allon, T Cunningham, G Reilly, W Whitehurst

DATES . . . 2

561 Fairs Cup victory in Budapest
562 Newcastle United 1 Hereford United 2
563 Newcastle United 3 Sunderland 1 (Beardsley 3)
564 Newcastle United 3 Manchester City 1 FA Cup final (the Revie Plan beaten)
565 Newcastle United 13 Newport Co. 0 (Shackleton's debut with 6 goals)
566 Newcastle United 9 Southport 0
567 Newcastle United 1 Chelsea 0 (record gate on Gallacher's return)
568 West Ham 8 Newcastle United 1 (with three goalkeepers)
569 Newcastle United 1 QPR 0 (Keegan debut)
570 Newcastle United 4 Forest 3 (FA Cup game annulled)

UNITED IN THE FA CUP . . . THE FIFTIES

571 16 games

572 York City
573 Hillsborough, Sheffield
574 Rotherham United
575 Bobby Mitchell
576 Nottingham Forest
577 Sunderland
578 Manchester City, Fulham
579 1955
580 Huddersfield Town (1955)

581 Hendon at Vicarage Road, Watford
582 False. United's only victory, 4-3 v. Forest, was wiped from the records
583 Frank Clark
584 Alex Bruce
585 United won 2-1 in the final of the Texaco Cup
586 J Tudor, M Macdonald, S Barrowclough
587 Pat Howard was sent off, Bob Moncur scored
588 Goodison Park, Everton. Malcolm Macdonald scored
589 Tommy Gibb replaced Jimmy Smith
590 A Kennedy, T McDermott joined Liverpool; K Keegan joined United

591 Sammy Weaver
592 Neil Harris
593 FA Cup, 1910
594 Jimmy Richardson
595 Jimmy Lawrence
596 Tommy Robson
597 Bill McCracken
598 Winning promotion in 1965. Back row: J Iley, F Clark, D Hilley, W Penman. Front row: B Cummings, T Knox, D Craig, B Robson, S Anderson, J McGrath, J Harvey

599 Stewart Mitchell and Jackie Bell

600 v. Luton Town, Willie McFaul and Pat Howard

UNITED TEASERS . . . I

601 Bob Moncur

602 Joe Allon, Kevin Scott

603 Ivor Allchurch

604 Joe Allon

605 John Craggs (in two spells)

606 Tony Cunningham, Mick Harford, Imre Varadi

607 Geoff Nulty

608 R Simpson (Celtic), F Clark (Nottingham Forest), P Withe, P Heard (Villa), K Keegan, T McDermott, A Kennedy, H Gayle (Liverpool)

609 Queen rock concert attracted 38,000

610 Atletico Mineiro and Botafogo (Brazil), Reykjavik (Iceland), Juventus (Italy), St Mirren, Dunfermline (Scotland), Notts County (England)

UNITED TEASERS . . . 2

611 Sporting Lisbon

612 Alan Gowling

613 Both were born in the Lancs town of Leyland

614 Notts County, Rabat Ajax (Malta)

615 Jimmy Greaves

616 Paul Stephenson

617 QPR

618 *Head Over Heels in Love*

619 K Keegan, J Charlton, I Allchurch, G Eastham

620 The game continued until the first side scored, that being United

TYNE v. WEAR

621 1979/80 (1-0 at Roker Park)

622 Newcastle United, York City, Sunderland, Manchester City. Manchester City defeated Sunderland
623 C Suggett, I Hughes, J Nelson, G Herd
624 Jim Pearson
625 1955/56
626 Gary Rowell 1978/79
627 Ollie Burton
628 Peter Beardsley, Alec Tait
629 S Anderson, D Elliott, R Robinson, J Clarke (A Franks was an amateur)
630 Ian Baird

GOLDEN OLDIES

631 Colin Veitch
632 He became the oldest debutant for England (35 years 6 months)
633 St James Park
634 Chillingham Road, Heaton
635 Tom Watson
636 Arsenal
637 Billy Hampson, 44 years 225 days (in 1927)
638 Aston Villa
639 Joe, John, Brian HARVEY
640 True

KEVIN KEEGAN

641 £100,000
642 63 caps
643 Scunthorpe United
644 SV Hamburg, Southampton, Newcastle United
645 Armthorpe, near Doncaster
646 He was arrested and beaten when on England tour
647 Nottingham Forest. He played for Hamburg
648 European Footballer of the Year

649 Spain

650 Trelford Mills

TRANSFER TRAIL

651 Glen Keeley

652 Albert Stubbins, Len Shackleton

653 Peter Withe

654 John Ryan (from Oldham)

655 Glyn Hodges

656 Santos, Botafogo

657 Barrie Thomas (£45,000)

658 David McKellar

659 Billy Whitehurst

660 Denis Laughton (of Morton)

CLUB FACTS . . . 2

661 1926/27, 25 victories

662 v. Newport County, 1946

663 League v. Burton Wanderers, Cup v. Aston Villa

664 Southport

665 Manchester City (60 wins)

666 Orient

667 True

668 Jackie Milburn

669 Yes (1906/07)

670 1977/78

UNITED FAMILIES

671 Chris and Ron Guthrie

672 George and Ted Robledo

673 Martin Thomas

674 They were capped for different countries . . . England and Wales

675 True. Harry of Liverpool guested for United during the War
676 Neil McDonald
677 Preston North End
678 Chris Waddle (cousin Alan Waddle)
679 Neil Harris (son John Harris)
680 Mick (51 caps) and Con Martin (30 caps)

CUP ASSORTMENT

681 Wolverhampton Wanderers (1908)
682 Geoff Nulty and Peter Noble
683 Glasgow Celtic
684 Thomas Nordahl
685 Burnley and Southampton
686 Goodison Park, Old Trafford
687 Oldham Athletic
688 Wrexham
689 R Simpson (2), J Fairbrother, W McFaul, M Mahoney
690 Blackburn Rovers

PHOTOFIT . . . 2

691 *Back row*: Craig, Mitchell, Barrowclough, Burkinshaw, Burleigh, Cassidy, Nattrass, Gibb. *Middle row*: Davies, Dyson, McNamee, Macdonald, Tudor, Clark, Smith, Burton. *Front row*: Young, Craggs, Moncur, Harvey, Foggon, Arentoft, Guthrie
692 *Back row*: Burton, Clark, McFaul, McNamee, Gibb, Craig, Davies. *Front row*: Scott, Sinclair, Robson (B), Elliott, Robson (T)
693 *Back row*: Connolly, Hardwick, Carr, Manners, Barton. *Middle row*: Brownlie, Nicholson, Cassidy, Suggett, Scott, Mitchell, Pearson, Mulgrove, Robinson, Davies, Shoulder, Bird. *Front row*: Cartwright, Martin, Withe, Walker, McGarry, Hibbitt, Nattrass, Wharton

694 *Back row*: Iley, Burton, Craig, Anderson, Marshall, Clark, Cummings, Thompson, McGrath. *Front row*: Hockey, Hilley, McGarry, Harvey, Penman, Allen, Suddick

695 *Back row*: Scoular, Cowell, Thompson, Paterson, Mitchell, Crowe. *Front row*: Milburn, Broadis, McMichael, White, Curry

696 *Back row*: Neale, Thompson, Hollins, McKinney, Dalton, Ferguson. *Front row*: Hilley, Hale, Thomas, Kerray, Fell

697 *Back row*: Cowell, Harvey, Simpson, Brennan, McMichael, Robledo (T). *Front row*: Walker, Foulkes, Milburn, Robledo (G), Mitchell

698 Sam Weaver (Back, second from right). Ron Starling (Front, second from right)

699 *Back row*: Davies, McGarry, McNamee, McFaul, Gibb, Porterfield (Sunderland). *Front row*: Green, Smith, Dyson, Guthrie, Allen

700 *Back row*: McCracken, Low, Shepherd, McWilliam, Carr. *Front row*: Rutherford, Howie, Veitch, Higgins, Wilson, Whitson. *Ground*: F Watt (sec), Lawrence, J P Oliver (Director)

NICKNAMES . . . 2

701 Peter Beardsley
702 Bill Appleyard
703 Ray Blackhall
704 Jimmy Stewart
705 Kit Napier
706 Frank G Watt
707 "Gnasher"
708 David McCreery
709 Paul Goddard
710 "Jinky"

MASTER CHALLENGE . . . 1

711 Sammy Weaver

712 Arthur Cox
713 Duggie Livingstone
714 Ray Wood (Manchester United), George King (Port Vale, England "B")
715 Derek Kevan
716 Billy Merideth (Manchester City in the 1924 FAC semi-final)
717 Micky Burns and Frank Clark
718 Peter Morris
719 Norman Smith
720 Alan Kennedy, 19 years 8 months in the 1974 FA Cup final

INSTANT RECALL . . . SEASON 1987/88

721 P Digweed, T Wright
722 Tottenham Hotspur
723 Chelsea, Gary Kelly
724 Tony Cunningham for Blackpool
725 Mark Hateley (for Monaco)
726 N McDonald, P Gascoigne
727 Kenny Wharton, Paul Gascoigne
728 Paul Gascoigne
729 v. Stoke City reserves. No, he didn't score
730 v. Watford (home, April). The players are P Gascoigne (100), K Wharton (300), D McCreery (400)

UNITED GOALKEEPERS

731 J Lawrence, D Hollins, M Thomas, W McFaul, M Kingsley
732 M Mahoney, R Simpson
733 Martin Burleigh
734 John Hope
735 Bill Bradley
736 Micky Burns

737 Kevin Carr
738 Roger Jones (Blackburn Rovers)
739 Eric Steele
740 Ronnie Simpson (on Celtic)

MIXED BAG . . . 3

741 Arsenal
742 J Milburn, R Mitchell
743 D McCreery, S Carney
744 False
745 Blyth Spartans v. Wrexham FA Cup 5th Round replay
746 Keith Burkinshaw
747 Joe Harvey
748 Gary Megson and Don Megson (Sheffield Wednesday 1966)
749 Bradford Park Avenue, Lincoln City, Newport County
750 Chris Waddle

MIXED BAG . . . 4

751 Roy Bentley
752 Wolves, Watford
753 Kevin Todd
754 Grant Malcolm
755 Ronnie Williams (1935 v. England)
756 Dave Hollins
757 Ollie Burton
758 H Bedford, M/R Blackburn, H Bolton
759 United's train was derailed in the Yorkshire Dales
760 Dalglish's first goal for Liverpool at Anfield

MIX-UP . . . 2

761 Terry McDermott

762 Gary Kelly
763 Colin Suggett
764 Peter Withe
765 Bill Appleyard
766 George Hannah
767 Tommy Walker
768 Liam Tuohy
769 Alan Davies
770 Peter Beardsley

WELSH CONNECTION

771 Tom Evans (1928)
772 Alan Davies
773 W Davies, K Leek, R Williams
774 Trevor Hockey
775 Martin Thomas
776 Wrexham (1977/78)
777 Ollie Burton
778 Glyn Hodges
779 W Foulkes, D Hollins, R Williams
780 Sunderland

REMEMBER SEASON . . . 1950/51

781 4th
782 B Cowell, J Fairbrother, T Walker
783 T Walker, E Taylor, J Milburn, G Robledo, R Mitchell
784 Bob Stokoe
785 Ronnie Simpson
786 Tottenham Hotspur
787 Bury, Bolton, Bristol Rovers, Blackpool
788 Alf McMichael
789 Hillsborough, Sheffield/Leeds Road, Huddersfield
790 George Robledo

AUTOGRAPHS . . . 2

791 Martin Thomas
792 Jimmy Scoular
793 Iam McFaul
794 Duncan Neale
795 Wesley Saunders
796 John Anderson
797 Frank Brennan
798 Ken Wharton
799 Len Shackleton
800 Jim Iley

UNITED IN THE FA CUP . . . THE EARLY YEARS

801 The Corinthians
802 Billy Hampson (1924)
803 Aberdare
804 Barnsley
805 George Robledo
806 Preston
807 Hartlepool
808 Sheffield United
809 Chelsea (1911, 1932)
810 Derby County

MALCOLM MACDONALD

811 Craven Cottage, Fulham
812 Tonbridge
813 £333,333.33
814 Fulham, Huddersfield Town
815 1972 v. Wales
816 St Étienne
817 Sweden (with Djorgarden)

818 Willie Hall (Spurs 1938), Cyprus
819 Consecutive goals record, 6 v. Cyprus, West Germany
820 A Rolls-Royce

WHERE DID THEY GO?

821 Swindon Town
822 Barrow
823 Arsenal
824 Bury
825 Birmingham City
826 Wolves
827 Huddersfield Town
828 Middlesbrough
829 Manchester City
830 Manchester City

PHOTOFIT ... 3

831 Malcolm Macdonald and Mick Channon
832 Dave Hilley
833 Albert Stubbins
834 Ivor Allchurch
835 Bobby Cummings
836 Glen Keeley
837 Barrie Thomas
838 Alan Suddick
839 Alex Bruce
840 Keith Dyson

BRAIN TESTERS ... 1

841 B Robson, I Mitchell, T Gibb
842 Birmingham City
843 The Guinness Six-a-side Competition (in Manchester)

844 The Rolling Stones, Bruce Springsteen, Bob Dylan, Queen
845 Bishop Auckland v. Crook Town
846 Aberdeen, Hibernian
847 Jimmy Scoular
848 Six times. United never won there
849 Bo'ness, Armadale
850 Victor Nogueria

BRAIN TESTERS . . . 2

851 Ray Xuereb
852 One of few modern players to have appeared in every round of the FA Cup, including qualifying stages
853 J Charlton (1966), Bill McGarry (1954)
854 Aston Villa (1905, 1924), Manchester City (1955, 1976), Arsenal (1932, 1952)
855 1-1
856 Albert Shepherd
857 Everton
858 Tottenham Hotspur
859 Gales. Due to possible damage to United's old West Stand
860 Swindon Town (1910)

JACKIE MILBURN

861 1943
862 Player-manager
863 Yiewsley (or now Hillingdon Borough), Ipswich Town
864 John, Edward, Thompson
865 He netted after 45 seconds, the quickest in a final since the turn of the century
866 George, Jim, Jack Milburn (all Leeds), Stan Milburn (Chesterfield, Leicester)
867 No. He played in the number 9 shirt in 1951, 1952, but in the number 8 shirt in 1955, Vic Keeble wearing the number 9 jersey

868 1947 (v. Bury)
869 He scored a hat-trick
870 Northern Ireland

REMEMBER SEASON . . . 1964/65

871 Good Friday
872 Tommy Knox
873 Swindon Town
874 Dave Hilley
875 Stan Anderson
876 Bury
877 Wyn Davies, Francis Lee
878 F Clark, G Marshall, D Craig, S Anderson, J McGrath
879 Ron McGarry
880 Jim Iley

SCOTS CONNECTION . . . 2

881 Alex Cropley
882 Ronnie Simpson
883 R S McColl
884 Bob Moncur, Jimmy Scoular
885 D Jackson, A Craig, G Reilly, D McKellar, R McKinnon
886 John Blackley (with Hibs)
887 Hughie Gallacher, George Reilly
888 John Brownlie
889 Dave Hilley (Third Lanark)
890 Dundee United

SAME NAMES . . . 3

891 Smith
892 Stewart
893 Taylor

894 Thomas
895 Wilson
896 Craig
897 Scott
898 Allen
899 Anderson
900 Gibson

PHOTOFIT...4

901 Charlie Wayman
902 George Luke
903 Dick Keith and Colin Taylor (Walsall)
904 J Sinclair, J Scott, O Burton, P Arentoft, W Davies. The trophy is the Inter Cities Fairs Cup
905 Bobby Cummings and Brian Harvey of Northampton Town
906 Tommy Gibb and George Best (Manchester United)
907 Vic Keeble
908 Kevin Todd
909 Ted Robledo
910 Wyn Davies of Bolton Wanderers

UNITED STRIKERS...2

911 Alan Gowling (30 goals, 1975/76)
912 Malcolm Macdonald
913 Paul Goddard
914 Billy Whitehurst
915 Ron McGarry
916 Barrie Thomas
917 Willie Penman
918 Alan Shoulder
919 John Evans Wright Sinclair
920 Wyn Davies

MAGPIE ASSORTMENT . . . 3

921 Frank Clark
922 T Green, R Simpson
923 Terry McDermott
924 Tommy Pearson
925 Scottish (b. Edinburgh)
926 David Ford
927 Alan Gowling
928 Mick Harford. One hour in March 1982 before signing for Birmingham City
929 Willie Penman, Joe Butler, Peter Noble (with Swindon)
930 Jimmy Scoular

JOE HARVEY

931 Doncaster
932 Bradford City
933 True
934 1951, 1952 as a player, 1974 as a manager
935 Crook Town
936 June 1962
937 1974/75
938 United won the Fairs Cup on 11 June 1969, his birthday
939 Aberdeen, Dundee United
940 Company Sergeant-Major

LOOSE ENDS . . . 2

941 Alan Foggon
942 1984/85
943 George Robledo
944 Hong Kong
945 Dynamo Kiev, Moscow Dynamo, Moscow Torpedo
946 Manchester City
947 SC Internacional

948 Paul Cannell
949 Chelsea, Sheffield Wednesday
950 Terry and Kenny Hibbitt (Newcastle v. Wolves)

FIRST NAMES . . . 2

951 Malcolm Brown
952 Albert Franks
953 Peter Johnson
954 Charlie Spencer
955 David Smith

SECOND NAMES . . . 2

956 Keith Kettleborough
957 Brian Harvey
958 Tommy Cavanagh
959 Charlie Wayman
960 John McNamee

MISCELLANY . . . I

961 Stan Seymour on Jack Charlton's resignation as manager in 1985. (*The Book of Football Quotations*, Ball/Shaw)
962 QPR (1984/85), West Ham (1960/61)
963 J Milburn, M Macdonald, A Shepherd
964 Stade Rennais
965 Gordon Lee (*The Book of Football Quotations*, Ball/Shaw)
966 J Meadows (Manchester City), W Barnes (Arsenal) (1955, 1952)
967 North America, Canada and USA
968 The John White Award, for best-behaved supporters
969 Tommy Craig
970 Len Shackleton, on Newcastle United (*The Book of Football Quotations*, Ball/Shaw)

MISCELLANY ... 2

971 Jim Iley
972 Japan XI, Syria XI, Yamaha, Botafogo
973 Alan Shoulder (9 penalties, 1979/80)
974 George Burley
975 Bela Vista (Brazil)
976 Huddersfield Town
977 True (in December 1942)
978 Gary Walton
979 Willie McFaul (a penalty v. Pesci Dosza, 1971, in the shoot-out)
980 W McFaul, C Suggett, J Harvey, J Pickering

FA CUP TEASERS

981 It was played at Maine Road because of crowd trouble the year before
982 Nottingham Forest, 1-1
983 Nottingham Forest (15 games)
984 Charlton Athletic
985 Manchester City, WBA, Charlton Athletic, Wolves, Wimbledon
986 Bedford Town, Hereford United, Wigan Athletic, Hendon
987 J Milburn, B Cowell, B Mitchell
988 1952
989 Aston Villa, Tottenham Hotspur (7 wins)
990 Bolton Wanderers, 2-1 win

MASTER CHALLENGE ... 2

991 The referee in the 1932 Cup final who gave United the "Over the line goal"
992 Eintracht Frankfurt
993 Mr J Rush

994 George Martin
995 Derek Wright (Physio)
996 Roy Bentley
997 J Clarke, G Roeder
998 John Dixon (Aston Villa), Ray Wood (Manchester United)
999 Andy Aitken
1000 Ron McGarry

MASTER CHALLENGE . . . 3

1001 H Gallacher (39), T McDonald (23), S Seymour (19)
1002 Peter McWilliam (United 1910, Spurs 1921)
1003 Colin Clish
1004 Rex
1005 A Dominican priest, Father Dalmatius Houtmann
1006 Arthur Cox (January 1981, March 1984)
1007 Charlie Wayman
1008 Leo Houtsonan
1009 Winston Churchill
1010 Lido Vieri

STOPPAGE TIME

1011 George Eastham (35 years 5 months, for Stoke City)
1012 Tom Phillipson (Mayor during the 1940s)
1013 Workington Town
1014 Ray Clemence (for Spurs, September 1985)
1015 Sid Blake (1905-09)
1016 Bury (to avoid losing their place in the Central League, they drew 2-2 and stayed in the competition)
1017 Norman Smith
1018 Mick Martin (for Eire)
1019 It was the first season ever United did not field a Scot
1020 Bob Hewison